REGENERATION IN VERTEBRATES

The Developmental Biology Conference Series, 1956

HELD UNDER THE AUSPICES OF

THE NATIONAL ACADEMY OF SCIENCES

NATIONAL RESEARCH COUNCIL

Paul Weiss

ORGANIZER AND GENERAL CHAIRMAN

THE CONFERENCES

EMBRYONIC NUTRITION

Brown University, July 23–24

Chairman: J. S. NICHOLAS; *Reporter and editor:* DOROTHEA RUDNICK

REGENERATION IN VERTEBRATES

Brown University, July 23–24

Chairman: E. G. BUTLER; *Reporter and editor:* CHARLES S. THORNTON

CYTODIFFERENTIATION

Brown University, July 27–31

Chairmen: ERNST HADORN, HOLGER HYDÉN, W. S. ANKEL, V. B. WIGGLESWORTH, *and* ISAAC BERENBLUM; *Reporter and editor:* DOROTHEA RUDNICK

ENVIRONMENTAL INFLUENCES ON PRENATAL DEVELOPMENT

Jackson Memorial Laboratory, August 2–4

Chairman: MEREDITH N. RUNNER; *Reporter and editor:* BEATRICE MINTZ

IMMUNOLOGY AND DEVELOPMENT

Jackson Memorial Laboratory, August 7–9

Chairman: JAMES D. EBERT; *Reporter and editor:* MAC V. EDDS, JR.

PHYSIOLOGY OF INSECT DEVELOPMENT

Macdonald College, August 14–16

Chairman: MAX F. DAY; *Reporter and editor:* FRANK L. CAMPBELL

DYNAMICS OF PROLIFERATING TISSUES

Brookhaven National Laboratory, September 5–8

Chairman: C. P. LEBLOND; *Reporter and editor:* DOROTHY PRICE

ENDOCRINES IN DEVELOPMENT

Shelter Island, N.Y., September 11–13

Chairman: B. H. WILLIER; *Reporter and editor:* RAY L. WATTERSON

MITOGENESIS

Argonne National Laboratory, September 24–26

Chairman: AUSTIN M. BRUES; *Reporters and editors:* H. S. DUCOFF *and* C. F. EHRET

WOUND HEALING AND TISSUE REPAIR

Rockefeller Institute, October 2–4

Chairman: FRANCIS D. MOORE; *Reporter and editor:* W. BRADFORD PATTERSON

Symposium on Regeneration in Vertebrates, Brown University, 1956.

REGENERATION IN VERTEBRATES

Edited by

CHARLES S. THORNTON

THE UNIVERSITY OF CHICAGO PRESS

The Library of Congress Catalog Card

SYMPOSIUM ON REGENERATION IN VERTEBRATES,
Brown University, 1956.

Regeneration in vertebrates, edited by Charles S. Thornton. [Chicago] University of Chicago Press [1959]

xi, 107 p. illus. 24 cm. (The Developmental biology conference series, 1956)

Condensed version of the proceedings of the conference.
Bibliography: p. 99–107.

1. Regeneration (Biology) 2. Vertebrates. I. Thornton, Charles Stead, 1910– ed. II. Title. (Series)

QH499.S94 1956 596 59–8869

Library of Congress

THE UNIVERSITY OF CHICAGO PRESS, CHICAGO 37
Cambridge University Press, London, N.W. 1, England
The University of Toronto Press, Toronto 5, Canada

Composed and printed by THE UNIVERSITY OF CHICAGO PRESS
Chicago, Illinois, U.S.A.

Preface to the Series

Development and growth have usually been studied rather piecemeal: as embryology, or plant physiology, or nutrition, or oncology; as seriation of stages of chick embryos, as cell division in fish eggs or plant root tips, as growth curves of children, as hormone response of plumage, as spread of a fungus, as repair of a broken bone or the swelling of a diseased spleen; by observation, measurement, comparison, chemical alteration, excision, transplantation, or sheer speculation. Yet, in reality, all these are merely isolated aspects of one broad continuous spectrum of phenomena, varied manifestations of the same basic principles and elementary processes—multiplication of organic mass (growth); diversification of that mass (differentiation); pattern formation (morphogenesis); progressive change (maturation and aging); and the repair or reproduction of patterns after disturbance (regulation and regeneration).

This unity of subject matter has received renewed emphasis in the "Developmental Biology Conference Series of 1956," a record of which is now presented in ten volumes, including the present report. The series consisted of co-ordinated and interdisciplinary conferences, symposia, and workshops, organized under the sponsorship of the Biology Council of the Division of Biology and Agriculture, National Academy of Sciences–National Research Council, with the generous financial support of governmental agencies, industrial organizations, and private foundations and donors (see list at end of Preface).

The Conference Series brought together experts from the fields of anatomy, biochemistry, biometry, biophysics, botany, cytology, embryology, endocrinology, genetics, histology, immunology, microbiology, neurology, nutrition, oncology, pathology, physiology, radiology, and zoölogy, from the United States and abroad, less for a display of most recent technical advances than for a concerted examination and evaluation of the contributions of these various specialties to the elucidation of focal issues of developmental biology. Fresh orientation and new ideas could be expected to emerge from this pool of critically distilled knowledge by the intersection of formerly unrelated trends of thought or by the discovery of common cores in formerly unrelated sets of data. Nearly three hundred American and fifty-four foreign scientists (from nineteen countries) joined in this task.

To serve the outlined objective, the meetings had to be ruled by the key words: *perspective* and *relevance.* All participants were admonished to present only such itemized information, conclusions, demonstrations, criticisms, illustrations, questions, and quotations as promised to throw light on the *issue* under discussion; that is, to confine themselves to comments of "strategic" or "catalytic" pertinence, not merely adding to the bulk of information, but contributing to clarification, order, harmonization, and comprehensibility. Pertinent comments, however, were welcomed regardless of whether they referred to data so new as to be still largely unknown; so old as to have been widely forgotten; so specialized or technical as to have received limited currency among "outsiders"; so theoretical as to have escaped the practitioners; or so "self-evident" as to have evaded critical scrutiny. Each participant was expected to draw from his store of special knowledge points that might help correct misinterpretations, indicate the feasibility of new approaches, and, above all, reveal existing gaps of knowledge and understanding.

It is evident that a group exercise of this complexion, with free give-and-take, could not possibly "cover the ground" in any of the selected topics within the given time limits and without sacrificing spontaneity, informality, and depth of penetration. Often a few key issues, profoundly analyzed and critically elucidated, proved far more enlightening than a hurried bird's-eye view of a large field. In cases in which workers from different disciplines were only vaguely acquainted with one another's stock-in-trade and vocabulary, the time and effort spent describing even elementary facts in order to provide a common ground for communication proved very worthwhile indeed. In other instances, where the facts were familiar but their interpretation was controversial, it seemed preferable to let argumentation take precedence over the recital of facts.

The foregoing remarks are intended to explain the discursive nature of these volumes. In conferences which combine basic and clinical interests, technical and theoretical approaches, molecular and organismic concepts, botanical and zoölogical subjects, biochemical and morphological aspects, it is imperative to place the reconciliation and synthesis of viewpoints above all other considerations.

In line with this general precept, each conference chairman was to open his meeting with a brief keynote address, staking out the major problems for discussion. By phrasing questions, rather than stating theses, he was to set the stage for free, though not necessarily unpremeditated, participation. Most of the conferences were closed meetings, with attendance confined to the invited panel members. In a few cases, auditors were admitted. Only the symposia at Brown University, which were co-sponsored by the International Union of Biological Sciences, were open to the general public.

For the purpose of publication, an experienced scientist familiar with the subject matter was appointed as official reporter and editor for each conference, to attend all sessions without taking part in the discussions. From the sound-tape recordings of the proceedings and his or her own notes, each editor then produced a condensed version of the conference. These accounts constitute the substance of this series of publications.

The individual reports vary greatly in form, depending on the topic and organization of each conference, as well as on the personal predilections of the editor. Only in one instance has the dialogue style been kept, and even so, only after considerable pruning. In other cases, an entire conference has been reported as a third-person account, reordering the text rather liberally into a logical sequence by combining related fragments; in this process of synthesis, an editor assumed the full prerogatives of an author. Most of the reports, however, range somewhere between these two extremes, abstracting the major comments of the various participants without obliterating their identity, yet resorting to verbal quotations infrequently or not at all. Some participants furnished their own rewritten versions of the factual presentations, and these were in most cases inserted in the text as such. In all cases, the participants were given an opportunity to check their respective contributions, either in the original transcript or later in the condensed and revised text.

The lack of uniformity reflects the informal spirit of the meetings and accents the main theme of the Conference Series: that developmental biology is currently in a state of flux, fitting no rigid mold and shaping its own course as it gains momentum by the growth and confluence of its many tributaries. It is hoped that the publication of this series will add to that momentum, as did the conferences themselves.

To each of the participants and, above all, to the chairmen and editors we owe a deep debt of gratitude. To the following donors of funds, we reiterate our appreciation for generous assistance: Atomic Energy Commission, U.S. Departments of the Air Force, Army, and Navy (Medical Services); Office of Naval Research; Fulbright Fellowship Program; National Institutes of Health; National Science Foundation; International Union of Biological Sciences; American Cyanamid Company; Diamond Alkali Company; Merck and Company, Inc.; Chas. Pfizer and Company, Inc.; Rohm and Haas Company; E. R. Squibb and Sons; American Cancer Society; and Rockefeller Foundation. Special thanks are due to Dr. Russell B. Stevens, executive secretary of the Biology Council, for carrying the major load in the recording of the conferences; and to Mrs. Geraldine A. Norton, administrative assistant, for her effective help with the preparations and practical details of the meetings.

PAUL WEISS

NEW YORK CITY
May 1958

SYMPOSIUM ON

Regeneration in Vertebrates

HELD JULY 23–24, 1956, AT BROWN UNIVERSITY
Providence, Rhode Island

Arranged by E. G. BUTLER
Princeton University,
Princeton, New Jersey

Presiding chairmen:

B. I. BALINSKY
University of the Witwatersrand, Union of South Africa

F. E. LEHMANN
University of Bern, Switzerland

Reporter and editor CHARLES S. THORNTON
Kenyon College, Gambier, Ohio

Participants:

D. T. CHALKLEY, *University of Notre Dame, Notre Dame, Indiana* (Present address: *National Cancer Institute, Bethesda, Maryland*)

HOWARD HOLTZER, *University of Pennsylvania, Philadelphia, Pennsylvania*

O. E. SCHOTTÉ, *Amherst College, Amherst, Massachusetts*

MARCUS SINGER, *Cornell University, Ithaca, New York*

L. S. STONE, *Yale University, New Haven, Connecticut*

H. A. L. TRAMPUSCH, *University of Amsterdam, Holland*

Discussion leaders:

E. G. BUTLER, *Princeton University, Princeton, New Jersey*

J. J. KOLLROS, *State University of Iowa, Iowa City, Iowa*

R. W. REYER, *University of Pittsburgh, Pittsburgh, Pennsylvania*

A. STEFANELLI, *University of Rome, Rome, Italy*

C. S. THORNTON, *Kenyon College, Gambier, Ohio*

PAUL WEISS, *Rockefeller Institute, New York, New York*

Contents

Introduction

E. G. BUTLER
Providence, Rhode Island

During the last decade there has been a greatly renewed interest in one of the oldest subjects in experimental zoölogy—regeneration in vertebrates. An increasing number of workers has entered the field, new materials and techniques have been employed, and, I think it is fair to say, no other period has witnessed greater advances. However, many of the basic factors underlying regenerative activity continue to remain obscure. It seems highly desirable that we now make an assessment of some of the recent advances in our understanding of the problems concerned, to see where we stand and to chart further programs of study.

Clearly, in a symposium occupying only two half-days it will be impossible to cover the field in a truly comprehensive manner. It is necessary—and undoubtedly it is desirable—to concentrate on those structures which have been most extensively subjected to experimental analysis and to give attention to those methods of approach which have proved most fruitful. This is the basis on which this symposium has been organized.

Anyone working in the field of vertebrate regeneration, regardless of the structure or structures with which he deals, soon discovers that he must not only take into account the local features of regenerative activity but likewise give attention to the organismic influences that are involved. These two aspects of regeneration have long been recognized as inseparable, and together they constitute, with respect to any structure, what may properly be referred to as a "regenerating system." For purposes of investigation, however, it is at times necessary to concentrate first on one part of the system and then on the other. Likewise, in this symposium we shall deal more specifically in the first session with the cellular basis of regenerative activity, with respect particularly to the eye, the tail, and the limb. We shall then progress in the second session to consider in some detail such major organismic influences as those exerted by the nerves and by the various hormones of the body. Finally, we shall take into account a technique which has been widely used in recent years, that of irradiation—a technique which has proved to be a valuable tool, especially in furthering our understanding of the relationships between the local and organismic aspects of the "regenerating system."

I wish to thank the main speakers who are taking part in this symposium and also those who are serving as discussion leaders. Particularly, I wish to express the pleasure we all feel in having as participants in the symposium so many of our European colleagues whose work we know so well and regard so highly.

· I ·

Regeneration of the Retina, Iris, and Lens[1]

L. S. STONE
Yale University School of Medicine

For many years I have used the eye of the vermilion spotted newt, *Triturus viridescens,* as a tool for studying the organization and development of the visual mechanism and for uncovering some of the fundamental factors governing regeneration. For the brief time at my disposal I shall confine my discussion largely to the findings of my own experiments, both published and unpublished, dealing with the eye of this adult newt. My attention will be centered upon the regeneration of the iris, lens, and neural retina, for, with this salamander, experiments can be devised to show that all three structures will regenerate from the same source, namely, the retina pigment epithelium. These cells are unique as an outstanding example of a specialized cell which can be followed from stage to stage as it changes its morphology and function to give rise to several totally different structures. I have often referred to this in previous publications. For the most complete and thorough survey of the regeneration of the lens I refer you to the recently published excellent review by Reyer (1954).

REGENERATION OF NEURAL RETINA FROM RETINA PIGMENT CELLS

Regeneration of the neural retina from retina pigment epithelium can be demonstrated very easily in the amphibians, especially in the urodeles (Stone, 1947, 1950*a, b, c*). It also has been shown to occur in anurans by a graduate student of mine, Dr. Katherine van Aken Smith in 1950 (unpublished) and recently by Sato (1953) in transplants of retina pigment cells in tadpole eyes of *Rana temporaria.*

Long ago—in fact, in 1924—I first observed the degeneration of the neural retina in transplanted eyes of the adult newt within 3 weeks after

[1] These investigations were aided by research grants (B-23 C7) from the National Institute of Neurological Diseases and Blindness of the National Institutes of Health, U.S. Public Health Service, and the Medical Fluid Research Fund of the Yale University School of Medicine.

operation. This was followed by regeneration of a new neural retina from the surviving retina pigment cells. Vision returned as soon as a newly regenerated optic nerve reached the brain. Since normal or abnormal vision depended upon the orientation of the graft (Stone, 1944, 1947, 1950*a*), the adult salamander eye proved to be an important tool for studying the functional organization in the retina, a subject which I shall not have time to include in this discussion.

We can also observe very clearly the regeneration of the neural retina from retina pigment cells by first removing the entire intact neural retina through a large opening in the dorsal wall of the eye (Stone, 1950*b*, Fig. 1) and then following the early changes in the denuded retina pigment cells as they proliferate non-pigmented cells that eventually differentiate into a functioning retina. Also fully differentiated neural retina membranes will develop from retina pigment epithelium implanted into the eye chamber (Stone, 1950*b*) or into the body cavity (unpublished). Later we shall point out in this discussion that the retina pigment cells can still give rise to entirely different functioning structures under appropriate conditions.

LENS REGENERATION FROM THE DORSAL IRIS EPITHELIUM

But before we discuss the role of the retina pigment cells further, I should like to review the formation of lenses from the iris epithelium. Replacement of a lost lens by a budding process of the epithelium along the free margin of the dorsal iris in *Triturus* newts has been well known since it was first reported by Colucci in 1891. I have studied this phenomenon in salamanders extensively and have pointed out that it does not occur in many species of amphibians and that it has not been shown in other vertebrates (Stone and Sapir, 1940). Much confusion has arisen in the literature because all lens material has not been removed by some investigators at the time of the experiment. This has been due partly to the fact that the entire lens cannot be excised with the same ease in all species.

Recently we recorded an extensive study of the normal variations in the early stages of lens regeneration from the dorsal iris in the eye of the adult newt after simple lentectomy. Several hundred cases were preserved at close intervals during the first 2 months after operation, and many *toto* mounts of dissections were made and illustrated along with the histologic picture (Stone and Steinitz, 1953*a*, Figs. 3–22, *A*). They not only epitomize the chief features of lens regeneration in certain newt eyes from the early depigmentation of the dorsal iris to the detachment of the lens regenerates at the end of a month but also call attention to the occasional variations in the rate of regeneration and the amount of iris tissue contributing to the new lens.

Grafts taken from the mid-dorsal iris, including the pupillary margin, show the highest potential for lens regeneration. As one approaches 9 and 3 o'clock, lens regeneration in the iris graft approaches zero (Stone, 1952, Figs. 2 and 3). The entire ventral half of the iris possesses no lens-forming cells.

In studying lens regenerates from grafts, it is essential to know that slight wounds along the pupillary margin of the dorsal iris usually do not affect regeneration (Stone, 1954*a,* Fig. 1). However, if a wound is not perfectly healed before early lens regeneration begins, a partially double lens may result (Stone, 1954*a,* Fig. 5, *A*). On the other hand, one must keep in mind that fresh wounds along the pupillary margin of a mid-dorsal iris graft at the time of operation may seriously affect lens regeneration from the transplant. This can be illustrated in grafts of mid-dorsal iris tissue from which the pupillary margin has been removed. When transplanted immediately to lensless host eyes, small defective lenses develop from the grafts (Stone, 1954*a,* Fig. 2). If the pupillary margin is allowed to heal 4 days before transplantation to a lentectomized host eye, lens regeneration from the mid-dorsal iris graft is well defined and almost as rapid as the one from the host dorsal iris.

FORMATION OF MULTIPLE LENSES

Normally, only one lens regenerates from the free margin of the dorsal iris after lentectomy. However, more than one lens can be induced to develop by simply substituting a segment of mid-dorsal iris with a piece of non-lens-forming ventral iris in a lentectomized eye (Stone, 1953, Fig. 5). This separates two potential lens-forming areas, each of which gives rise to a lens. Implanted plastic membranes splitting the iris into segments can produce the same effects (unpublished).

It must be borne in mind that much of the dorsal iris besides the pupillary margin also possesses lens-forming cells. This can be shown experimentally by inserting plastic membranes in the regions of the dorsal iris to produce permanent accessory pupils (Stone, 1954*b*). Along their margins lens development can be released. These lenses are gradually smaller as the accessory openings approach the ora serrata. They also arise only from the dorsal iris region in accessory pupils lying in the temporal and nasal portions of the iris. Therefore, in lens regeneration we find a lens-forming area spreading from a central point, as in the case of limb reduplication.

A number of investigators have implanted pieces of mid-dorsal iris into lentectomized eyes, but only one lens develops from one portion of the graft, namely, the original pupillary margin (Stone, 1952). However, we know from our experiments that the other borders of the graft also possess lens-forming cells. One can, for example, force the upper ciliary region of the mid-dorsal iris graft to give rise to a lens if the pupillary margin is cut away and the graft of appropriate size is rotated 180° and implanted in an eye already prepared for it (Stone, 1954*a*, Fig. 3). The ciliary border of the transplant then becomes part of the pupillary margin in the host eye and gives rise to a lens. Even then in some cases a lens will develop from host iris on either side of the transplant.

INHIBITION OF LENS REGENERATION BY LIVING LENS TISSUE

I should point out at this time that lens regeneration is inhibited when the dorsal iris is in the presence of a normal living lens, even though the latter is derived from the eye of another species of salamander (Stone, 1953). I have also reported that the presence of a regenerating lens does not produce any inhibiting effect until its outer capsule is completely formed. At this time it is 25–30 days of age and is ready to detach from its source of origin, the dorsal iris (Stone, 1952, Fig. 6). These regenerates, though small, are as effective in inhibiting lens regeneration as is the original lens. Ordinary mechanical forces of the normal lens play no active inhibitory role, for the substitution of wax lenses, glass beads, and spherical masses of tissue for the original lens have no inhibiting effect upon lens regeneration (Stone, 1953).

The importance of the iris-lens relationship to lens regeneration is shown in the following two contrasting experiments. In the first of these an impermeable plastic membrane, Pliofilm, was implanted so that the dorsal iris was isolated in a separate chamber from that occupied by the normal lens (Stone, 1953, Fig. 8). The dorsal iris was then no longer bathed by the aqueous humor circulating around the lens. Under these conditions a lens developed from the dorsal iris just as well as in complete lentectomy. Plastic membranes of Dupont No. 600, permeable to water-soluble substances, produce the same effects (unpublished).

Related to these results are those of the second experiment, which produced complete inhibition of lens regeneration. Into lentectomized eyes aqueous humor from eyes containing normal lenses was injected daily for 20, 40, 60, and 90 days. Lens regeneration took place only after the cessation of the injection of aqueous humor (Stone and Vultee, 1949; Stone, 1953, Fig. 9). Aqueous humor from the same or different species of salamander eye is equally effective (unpublished). Daily injections of

Ringer's solution had no inhibiting effect. Therefore, lens regeneration appears to be inhibited in the dorsal iris when the latter is bathed in aqueous humor containing some substance given off in the presence of a living lens. This specific lens effect is taking place within the eye and not through the blood stream, for it is a well-known fact that the presence of a lens in one eye does not affect the lens regeneration in the opposite lentectomized eye. We are in the process of studying the chemical significance of this phase of the problem.

INFLUENCE OF THE NEURAL RETINA ON LENS REGENERATION

There is another tissue which has a powerful influence on the lens regeneration from the dorsal iris, that is, the neural retina. This has been intimated by other investigators (Spemann, 1905; Wachs, 1914; Zalokar, 1944). When the dorsal iris was excised and isolated from the neural retina by transplanting it to the body wall or body cavity (unpublished), I found only three feeble attempts at lens regeneration in more than one hundred grafts. When the iris was accompanied by retina pigment epithelium, which regenerated a membrane of neural retina, the iris then gave rise to a lens if the free pupillary margin lay near or touched the regenerated neural retina (unpublished).

One can isolate the iris in another way by inserting a disk of Pliofilm between it and the neural retina in a lentectomized eye (unpublished). If the disk is perfectly implanted and isolation is complete, no lens regenerates. However, if small amounts of the neural retina are included on the iris side of the membrane, usually small cataractous lentoids develop from the dorsal iris. From the results of these experiments a quantitative effect seems to be implied.

I have also noticed in my experiments that when the regenerating vitreous humor is densely stained and infiltrated with fibroblasts, no lens develops, even though a fully differentiated neural retina is present. The vitreous body in this case probably functions as a shield similar to an implanted plastic membrane.

The neural retina can be permanently eliminated by removing it along with the retina pigment epithelium through a large slit made in the dorsal wall of the eye (results unpublished). The lens was also removed in this experiment, leaving the iris intact. If a small amount of neural retina regenerates from a small patch of retina pigment not removed, a small lentoid may develop from the dorsal iris. If no neural retina regenerates, the iris will remain intact for a long period, with no lens regeneration. However, as soon as this dorsal iris is transplanted to a freshly lentectomized eye, it releases lens regeneration in the presence of an intact neural retina.

Some years ago Dr. Steinitz and I (1953*a*) removed the lens and neural retina on one side and the lens only on the other side in a large number of eyes of adult newts, to compare the rate of lens regeneration on the two sides. We found that the rate of lens regeneration and the size of lens regenerates were much retarded during the first month in eyes from which the neural retina had been removed. Lens regeneration became more rapid when the regenerating neural retina began to differentiate. It is obvious, then, that lens regeneration can be initiated but will go along more slowly in the presence of a regenerating neural retina and not nearly so rapidly as in the case of one in the presence of an intact retina. I noticed many years ago somewhat similar results in transplanted eyes where the neural retina and the lens undergo degeneration followed by regeneration.

INFLUENCE OF NEURAL RETINA ON POLARITY OF THE LENS REGENERATES

In ordinary lens regeneration from the dorsal iris, a fiber-forming pole is directed inward toward the neural retina, and the outer subcapsular epithelium behind the pupillary space faces toward the aqueous chamber, as in the case of the normal original lens. I have often noticed in many of my experiments that the neural retina appeared to be playing a role in establishing the polarity of the regenerating lens. Two experiments might be cited to illustrate this point.

One can excise a segment of mid-dorsal iris, turn it inside out (rotation 180° on dorsal-ventral axis), and heal it in place. Later the lens is removed to release lens regeneration (Stone, 1954*a,* Figs. 4 and 14). The lens regenerate, in spite of the rotated position of the dorsal iris, is oriented in the normal direction, with the fiber pole directed toward the neural retina.

In another series of experiments, of which there were many, plastic membranes were imbedded between the iris and the retina in lentectomized eyes. In all cases where there was a small portion of the neural retina included in the chamber on the iris side of the membrane, the fiber-forming pole of the lens regenerate was directed from the beginning toward the segment of neural retina (Stone, 1954*a,* Figs. 15–18).

REGENERATION OF IRIS AND LENS FROM IRIS TISSUE

The iris in most vertebrate eyes does not regenerate, but in the eyes of the adult newt it has a maximum capacity which I can easily illustrate.

In a series of experiments where varying amounts of dorsal iris were removed, complete regeneration took place (Stone and Griffith, 1954). The regenerating dorsal iris regenerated a lens at any time that the normal lens was removed. But, in these cases, regeneration was from iris tissue.

REGENERATION OF IRIS AND LENS FROM RETINA PIGMENT CELLS

Further experiments were done, removing either all the dorsal, all the ventral, or the entire iris, including the adjacent rim of retina, to test the ability of the retina pigment epithelium to regenerate iris tissue (Stone, 1955). When all the dorsal iris was removed, it was regenerated chiefly from the growth of the retina pigment epithelium along the wound margin. The lens always regenerated from the regenerating dorsal iris, depending upon the time at which the normal lens was removed.

The excised ventral iris was replaced in the same manner. However, it was obvious that the cut margins of the dorsal iris in the nasal and temporal regions also appeared to be contributing to the regenerating ventral iris (Stone, 1955, Fig. 3). To test whether or not some of the potential lens-forming cells were being carried into the non-lens-forming ventral region, grafts of the regenerating ventral iris in 48 eyes were placed in lentectomized eyes (Stone, 1955, Figs. 4 and 5). None of them regenerated lenses.

In another series of 14 eyes (98–100 days after iridectomy) a disk of Pliofilm was inserted into the pupillary space to separate the dorsal and ventral halves of the iris. The regenerated lens in each case was excised, to release lens regeneration both above and possibly below the membrane. In two cases (Stone, 1955, Fig. 6) a lens developed in the nasal and temporal regions from the regenerated ventral iris tissue, indicating that lens-forming cells had been brought in by the dorsal iris tissue during regeneration. In all cases the regenerating ventral iris did not possess the normally prominent protractor lentis muscle.

Other experiments show that the entire iris plus the adjacent rim of retina could be removed, followed by complete regeneration of iris and lens from the retina pigment cells (Stone, 1955, Figs. 7 and 28).

ROLE OF PITUITARY AND THYROID ON REGENERATION OF IRIS, LENS, AND NEURAL RETINA

It is well known that the removal of the pituitary and thyroid glands has a profound effect upon the regeneration of the tail and limbs of newts. Schotté (1953) and his co-workers (Schotté and Lindberg, 1954;

Schotté and Bonneville, 1955; Schotté and Chamberlain, 1955) have been reinvestigating this problem recently and have reported the importance of adrenal hormones in bringing about limb regeneration after hypophysectomy. Steinitz and I (1953*b*) found that regeneration of the neural retina and lens was retarded, but not inhibited, by the removal of either or both of the above-mentioned endocrine glands 5 days before the lens and retina were excised. There was, however, an increase in the number of cataracts compared with control experiments.

Schotté and Murphy (1953) essentially confirmed our results on lens regeneration in the same species of adult newts which were hypophysectomized simultaneously with lentectomy. Since the lens regenerated from an uninjured surface in contrast to that of a limb, they assumed that a different mechanism operated in initiating regeneration of these structures. However, I have found (unpublished) that when the dorsal iris is excised in hypophysectomized newts, both the iris and the lens will regenerate readily from either iris or retina pigment epithelium, as in the case of an animal possessing the pituitary gland.

ROLE OF RETINA PIGMENT IN LENS REGENERATION

Some years ago I transplanted into the eye chamber retina pigment membranes supported by the underlying choroid and scleral tissue (Stone, 1950*c*). These retina pigment grafts were dissected from various regions of the wall of the eye for the purpose of testing their ability to form neural retina membranes. At that time no notation was made of the exact region from which the grafts were taken. Many of them developed beautiful neural retina membranes, but none of them gave rise to lens tissue. Most of the implants were suspended in the vitreous chamber as tissue cultures without blood supply.

In 1951 Sato published his results of retina pigment grafts taken from the mid-dorsal part of the eye of adult *Triturus pyrrhogaster,* showing lens regenerates not associated with regenerating neural retina. He concluded that, since the retina pigment membranes were separated from their normal vascular environment, they were directed toward the formation of lenses instead of neural retina. So in 1952 I repeated my previous experiments with Steinitz (unpublished), taking most of the grafts this time from the mid-dorsal wall of the eye, a region similar to the one from which Sato obtained his pigment grafts. The grafts consisted of denuded retina pigment epithelium supported by the choroid layer and a portion of the sclera at one end. They were implanted into lentectomized eyes. A few similar grafts were taken from the ventral portion of the eye wall and implanted in the same manner. The retina pigment in these formed only neural retina.

Most of the grafts taken from the dorsal region of the eye also developed neural retina from the retina pigment epithelium. However, in a few cases only fully differentiated neural retina membranes were attached at one margin to well-defined lens regenerates. Therefore, both neural retina and lens can develop from the retina pigment epithelium in the same graft. Perhaps in some cases the thin membrane extending from the regenerating segments of neural retina, to which the lens regenerate was attached, can be considered a miniature iris.

In another group of experiments (results unpublished) an opening was made in the same region of the dorsal wall of the eye from which the above-mentioned grafts were taken. This was done by inserting a small piece of Pliofilm which penetrated the vitreous chamber. Before inserting the plastic membrane into the opening, a ring of surrounding neural retina was removed, to expose the retina pigment cells. Sometimes the plastic membrane was slowly eliminated, leaving the opening in the retina partially closed. From the thin margin of retina pigment surrounding the opening a small lens often developed. Regenerating neural retina often later closed in around the small lens regenerate.

From the results of the experiments which I have described, it is clear that the retina pigment epithelium is capable of giving rise to neural retina, iris, and lens. In our experiments we are mapping out the area containing the cells potential for lens formation. We can see that it has spread widely over the dorsal iris and dorsally into the retina pigment cells in an adult newt eye. From a developmental point of view it would be interesting to discover by the proper experiments whether or not the lens-inducing forces emanate largely or entirely from the dorsal portion of the optic vesicle. Since Dr. Reyer is making an extensive study of the mechanism of lens regeneration related to the embryological picture, perhaps some day he can give us an answer to this important question.

The chemical embryological studies of the lens made by the group of investigators in Amsterdam (Ten Cate and van Doorenmaalen, 1950; Woerdeman, 1953; Zuidweg, 1954) showing the early appearance and increase in the specific lens proteins by antiserum methods, the gradually changing chemical differentiation of glycogen, ribonucleic acid, and alpha-crystalline are of great importance to the whole lens problem. Of equal importance is the growth of our knowledge of the chemical activities of the fully differentiated lens. Special techniques with radioactive substances have been employed by Kinsey and his collaborators (Kinsey and Merriam, 1950; Merriam and Kinsey, 1950*a, b;* Frohman and Kinsey, 1952), at the Kresge Eye Institute, for studying rabbit lenses in vitro for longer than 2 weeks. Continuous synthesis and breakdown of proteins has been followed. Studies of this nature which can be applied to give us a clearer picture of the metabolism of both the lens and the retina will be essential before we can hope to solve the problem of lens regeneration.

DISCUSSION

Discussion leader: R. W. REYER, *School of Medicine, University of Pittsburgh*

In commenting on Dr. Stone's paper, DR. REYER pointed out that, since a large part of the symposium would be devoted to a consideration of limb regeneration, it would seem to be of interest to summarize the main differences between the regeneration of the lens or retina, as just described by Dr. Stone, and the regeneration of the limb. In the first place, lens regeneration during larval and adult stages appears to be restricted to the family Salamandridae. However, several species of urodeles and larval anurans are able to regenerate a new neural retina from the pigmented layer of the retina. Second, an initial stimulus of injury and wound healing is not necessary in lens regeneration, although it may play a role in retina regeneration. Third, during regeneration of a lens or retina, there is no blastema formed, at least in the usual sense of this term. Finally, the hormones of the thyroid gland and hypophysis affect mainly the rate of growth in size of the lens and neural retina, in contrast to their much more important role in limb regeneration, to be discussed later in this symposium by Dr. Schotté.

DR. REYER also discussed the question of dedifferentiation. In the case of the regeneration of the lens and neural retina, successive stages of this process can be very clearly demonstrated. These involve (1) loss of pigment from the iris or pigmented layer of the retina and, in the latter, cessation of pigment migration during light adaptation; (2) proliferation of these depigmented cells; and (3) their redifferentiation either into a lens or into neural retina. However, he pointed out that there are limitations to the extent of dedifferentiation taking place here. The new tissues formed from the pigmented epithelium were all of ectodermal origin in the embryo and are also parts of the same organ—the eye. The pigmented layer of the retina and of the iris therefore seems to represent a reserve source of cells capable of replacing either the lens or the neural retina.

DR. REYER observed that the action of normal lens tissue in inhibiting lens regeneration from the dorsal iris is of considerable interest, since it represents a clear case in which the development of a particular organ is inhibited by the presence of that same organ. This inhibition is apparently mediated by a diffusible substance present in the aqueous humor. In Dr. Stone's experiments, lens regeneration did occur, however, when the dorsal iris was isolated from the normal lens either with an impermeable Pliofilm membrane or with a semipermeable plastic membrane (Dupont No. 600). Therefore, this inhibitory substance, derived from the lens, must be composed of molecules large enough to resist passage through the latter membrane.

As a final point, DR. REYER stated that it has now been quite clearly established that the presence of a neural retina is necessary for lens regeneration from the iris. During ontogeny, the neural retina develops as an evaginated portion of the brain. Since the presence of an adequate number of nerves has been shown to be essential for limb and tail regeneration, it would be of importance to know whether the action of the neural retina in lens regeneration is similar in nature to the influence of nerves in limb regeneration. Some possibilities for the further study of this question, suggested by DR. REYER, would be the substitution for the neural retina of parts of the brain or of deviated, regenerating peripheral nerves as well as tissue culture of the dorsal iris, together with extracts of neural retina and other tissues.

During the general discussion of Dr. Stone's paper, DR. STEINBERG (Carnegie Institute) noted that, according to Dr. Stone's data, a lens regenerate apparently produced inhibitory substance only after the twenty-fifth day of its development. Two possible explanations might account for this: that the inhibitory substances are developed only after 25 days of lens growth or that a mass effect is involved. Has, DR. STEINBERG asked, Dr. Stone implanted into the eye two younger, smaller lenses whose total mass is equivalent to a 25-day lens? If so, does this inhibit lens regeneration from the dorsal iris? DR. STONE replied that it took the lens 25–28 days of growth to complete its morphogenesis and to become independent metabolically (its metabolic activities are anaerobic). This fact, he thought, had to be taken into account. Nevertheless, one could test the mass effect by getting larger lens regenerates from the use of tissues from other species of *Triturus*.

DR. LEHMANN (Bern) inquired whether only the retina pigment layer gave rise to the regenerate, and DR. STONE replied that this was true. The organized neural retina did not give rise to a regenerate, as its cells were fully differentiated and functioning. DR. LEHMANN also expressed interest in the phenomena of wound healing in the neural retina. What, for example, happens when an area of the neural retina is removed? DR. STONE pointed out that if a small area of the neural retina is excised, thus exposing the denuded retina pigment epithelium underneath, one gets local regeneration; a non-pigmented membrane will develop and differentiate, but never is there any activity seen in fully differentiated cells.

DR. BALINSKI (Witwatersrand) pointed out that even in early eye-cup stages the tapetum could transform into an entire eye cup, although the retina could not.

DR. LANGMAN (Amsterdam) referred to the work of Woerdemann and Ten Cate cited by Dr. Stone and stated that he and his associates had repeated this work and found antigens not only for the lens, as the above-cited investigators had found, but also for other parts of the eye, including the retina. He suggested that there might be a danger that one was working with antibodies against several proteins. In Dr. Langman's laboratory it was found that anti-alpha-crystalline antibody reacted specifically with iris and neural retina. He wished, therefore, to ask Dr. Stone whether he had found any difference with respect to alpha-crystalline between the dorsal iris and the rest of the iris. DR. STONE stated that he did not have this information.

DR. GOSS (Brown) then expressed interest in the influence of the neural retina on the polarity of the regenerating lens. He inquired whether the experiment had been performed of grafting beneath the cornea a piece of neural retina so that lens regeneration could respond to two polarities. Dr. Stone remarked that he had performed experiments of this nature but that the retina pigment membrane had fused with the iris and failed to form a neural retina. He mentioned other experiments in which the iris had been isolated by a membrane from the retina pigment layer for about 6 weeks. Then retina pigment cells were implanted into those eyes which had not regenerated a lens, to see whether the regenerating retina pigment membrane would produce lens regeneration. However, the retina pigment membrane here also fused with the iris.

· II ·

The Development of Mesodermal Axial Structures in Regeneration and Embryogenesis[1]

HOWARD HOLTZER[2]

Department of Anatomy, School of Medicine, University of Pennsylvania

INTRODUCTION

The axial structures of all vertebrates are characterized by a medial spinal cord surrounded by vertebrae. These in turn are flanked by the bilateral muscle masses. In this discussion emphasis is on the basic similarity between the regeneration of these structures in the salamander tail and their embryogenesis in all vertebrates. In regeneration, as in embryogenesis, the spinal cord conditions the histogenesis and morphogenesis of the adjacent mesodermal tissues. Specifically, whether we focus on the regenerating mesodermal axial structures of the salamander tail or on the embryonic formation of these structures in the mouse, chick, amphibian, or fish, it will be demonstrated that (1) the spinal cord induces the transformation of trunk mesodermal cells into cartilage cells; (2) the cartilage-promoting activity is confined to the motor half of the spinal cord and is transmissible through the intervening mesenchymal matrix; (3) the spinal cord determines the D-V axis and the general architecture of the cartilaginous vertebrae; and (4) the spinal cord conditions the axiation of the trunk structures.

The last portion of this paper is devoted to myogenesis. Here, too, the underlying unity of the developmental mechanisms responsible for myogenesis in most vertebrates will be stressed. From a serologic, cytologic, and histologic level, the details of trunk muscle formation in the regenerating salamander tail are remarkably similar to muscle formation in many vertebrate embryos.

1 Supported by research grants from the National Institute of Neurological Diseases and Blindness (B-493), of the National Institutes of Health, Public Health Service, and the Multiple Sclerosis Society.

2 American Cancer Society Scholar.

DESCRIPTIVE REVIEW OF THE REGENERATION OF THE SALAMANDER TAIL

Following amputation of the tail of a 20–35-mm. larval salamander, little is to be observed grossly for the first few days. This early period is best characterized as one of cell mobilization; the mechanism involved is cell migration. Intact epithelial sheets, as well as individual cells, partake in these movements. During this period the tissues of the stump undergo those changes that result in the activation and redistribution of cells that will contribute to the regenerated structure.

In a matter of hours the amputation surface is covered by the migratory wound epithelium. Mitotic figures are not abundant in the epidermis until the third or fourth postamputation day. Even at this late date the division figures are not confined to the epidermis in the region of amputation but extend anteriorly along the flank for a considerable distance. Twenty-four hours after amputation, the spinal canal is sealed off by movements of the cells in the ependymal layer (Stefanelli and Capriata, 1944). Again this migratory activity occurs independently of cell division.

Unlike the anuran notochord, the notochord of the salamander is incapable of regeneration. The incapacity to regenerate extends into the embryonic stages as well (Hadorn, 1952; Holtzer, 1952*c*). This feature is fortunate, for the traumatized surface of the notochord serves as a permanent and prominent marker of the original plane of amputation. The injured notochord is not invaded or degraded by macrophages.

The most dramatic changes of the early postamputation period are observed in the trunk muscles. Widespread dissolution of the myofibrillar material occurs within 24 hours after transection. Concurrently, the normal low-grade basophilia of the muscle is replaced by an extreme acidophilia. The second phase of sarcolysis (second through fourth postamputation days) involves the invasion of the injured muscle by leukocytes and macrophages. During this phase the degenerating muscle fibers are reduced to sacs of hyaline sarcoplasm, honeycombed by systemic cells. Regression of the trunk muscle may proceed up to two segments anterior to the amputation plane. The regressing muscle fibers appear to liberate individual muscle nuclei bounded by a scanty amount of cytoplasm. In staining properties (haematoxylin, azure-B, van Gieson, Mallory, and protargol) these emancipated muscle nuclei with their adherent cytoplasm merge with and are indistinguishable from the accumulating mesenchymal blastema cells. A similar sequence of changes has been described for adult mouse muscle following partial transection (Lash, Swift, and Holtzer, 1956).

Judging from the sectioned material, the major source of cells that form the mesenchymal blastema is derived from the erstwhile muscle nuclei and their adherent cytoplasm. However, it should be emphasized that the difficulties of cell identification with conventional histologic techniques preclude a decisive solution to the problem of the origin of blastemal cells. Nevertheless, two additional correlations are consistent with the possibility that the degenerating muscle fibers are the major source of mesenchymal blastema cells: (1) perceptible accumulation of blastema cells follows the degeneration of muscle fibers; (2) the early blastema cells first accumulate one or two segments anterior to the most posterior level of the spinal cord and notochord. This may be related to the fact that degeneration of the trunk muscles extends anterior to the plane of amputation. From this location the blastema cells spread posteriorly, eventually surrounding the regenerating spinal cord. Differentiated trunk cartilage cells cannot contribute significantly to the blastema, for they have not appeared in the tail at the time of amputation.

Overt regeneration of an axial tissue is first displayed by the elongation of the spinal cord by the sixth postamputation day. As diagramed in Figure 1, spinal cord and actively dividing mesenchymal blastema cells are the only tissues, other than epidermis, present in the regenerating tail at this time. By day 8 a small number of pro-cartilage cells aggregate to form a rod associated with the ventral portion of the regenerating spinal cord. Anteriorly, this pro-cartilage rod abuts on the surface of the non-regenerating notochord. Posteriorly, the pro-cartilage rod tapers to a point. Its most posterior extent lags several hundred micra behind the posterior tip of the regenerating spinal cord. In girth and location the newly formed pro-cartilage structure substitutes for the notochord. The pro-cartilage rod is well separated from the ventral surface of the spinal cord. Inspection of sectioned material suggests that the pro-cartilage rod is the product of active condensation of the mesenchymal blastema cells. Within the next several days the typical basophilic matrix and metachromatic capsules characteristic of mature hyaline cartilage form in that portion adjoining the notochord. At this time the first signs of incipient segmentation in the cartilaginous formation is evident (Holtzer, Holtzer, and Avery, 1955, Fig. 8). Further elongation of the cartilaginous structure is paced by the elongating spinal cord. The spinal cord and cartilaginous rod grow at the same rate throughout subsequent stages—approximately 0.8 mm/day. This means that in all stages the posterior tip of the cartilage lags several hundred micra behind the most posterior tip of the spinal cord. Differentiation of the cartilage proceeds

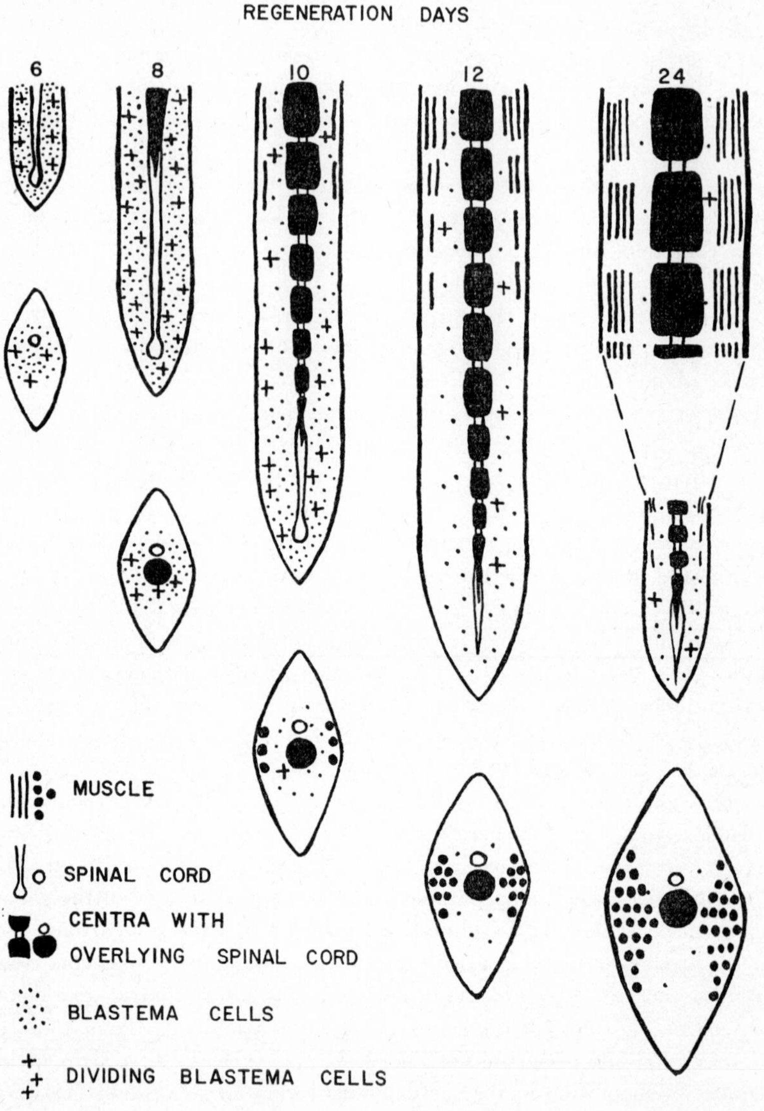

FIG. 1.—Diagrammatic representation of the major tissue relationships during normal regeneration of the tail. The upper row is a projection of the spinal cord and the notochord on a frontal section of the regenerated tail, taken at the mid-point of the D-V axis. Note the rapid growth of the spinal cord into the blastema. During all stages the neural tissue extends most posteriorly, followed by cartilage and muscle. The lower row represents cross-sections taken at the base of the regenerate.

in an anteroposterior direction. The posterior extension of the spinal cord and cartilage is accompanied by a corresponding distad displacement of the mesenchymal blastema.

Identifiable mononucleated myoblasts are first recognized around the eighth or ninth postamputation day. At this time they are associated with the formed muscle of the stump. This means that the earliest myoblasts actually form anterior to the amputation plane, for, as previously described, the muscle degenerates well anterior to the level of transection. Not until the tenth or eleventh day do small numbers of elongated myoblasts appear in the regenerate.

Further regenerative activity is a continuation of the events just outlined (see Holtzer, Holtzer, and Avery, 1955; S. Holtzer, 1956, for further details). From the twelfth day, spinal cord, segmented cartilaginous rod, and muscle elongate at an equal rate. Always the spinal cord extends most posteriorly, the cartilaginous rod next, and last the muscle, several hundred micra behind the tip of the cartilage. Meristematic growth is not found in any of the systems. For example, in the 6–30-day regenerating spinal cord the mitotic index is equal throughout its extent. Interestingly enough, the high mitotic index of the regenerating spinal cord extends anterior to the amputation plane. Similarly, the elongation of the cartilaginous rod is not referable to a meristematic growth tip. It has been suggested (Holtzer, Holtzer, and Avery, 1955) that elongation of the skeletogenous element reflects the continuous assimilation of blastemal cells into the cartilaginous rod in a manner analogous to the elongation of the tail of the chick described by Spratt (1955). The origin and mode of reproduction of muscle cells in the regenerated tail are uncertain (see last section).

Sections through a 25-day regenerated tail reveal that the cartilaginous structure beneath the spinal cord is segmented. Each cartilaginous segment represents a centrum. In older regenerated tails neural arches articulate with these segments. When stained with methylene blue, the cartilages are visualized as segmented, discontinuous structures. Histologically, the intersegment cartilage has a higher cell/matrix ratio than the hyaline cartilage of the segment. The regenerated muscle in the later stages is also segmented. However, the segmentation of the skeletal elements and the muscle fail to establish a constant relationship, suggesting that the segmentation of the two systems is independent.

EXPERIMENTAL ANALYSIS OF TAIL REGENERATION

a) Sequence of centrum and neural arch formation.—During normal development in the salamander, the cartilaginous neural arches are the first vertebral elements to appear; the cartilaginous centra do not develop until well after metamorphosis. During tail regeneration, formation of the cartilaginous centra precedes that of the neural arches. Does this reversal in sequence of formation of vertebral elements reflect fundamental differences in vertebral development in embryogenesis and regeneration? That this is not so is demonstrated by notochordectomy experiments performed on tail-bud embryos. Extirpation of the notochord in embryonic stages results in the precocious appearance of centra in young larvae. The absence of the notochord during embryonic development permits centra formation to precede that of the neural arches (Holtzer, 1952*c*). Thus in the salamander, if vertebrae develop in the absence of the notochord, either in the regenerating tail or in the embryo, centra are organized prior to neural arches. It may be of significance that in mammals, where the notochord is vestigial, centra appear earlier than neural arches (see, however, Avery, Chow, and Holtzer, 1955, and Lash, Holtzer, and Holtzer, 1957, for a slightly different relationship of the notochord to the centra in the chick).

b) *Dispensability of the notochord.*—The apposition of the forming cartilages with the stump of the notochord in the regenerating tail invited exploration of a possible relationship between these two structures. Are the cartilage cells in the regenerated tail derived from the notochord, as stated by Barfurth (1891)? Does the notochord determine the size or location of the cartilaginous centra? The following experiments demonstrated the inertness of the notochord of the stump with regard to regenerative events in the tail. A tunnel was prepared in the tail dorsal fin. A 3-mm. length of spinal cord, sandwiched between two pieces of trunk muscle, was introduced into this quasi-tissue culture chamber. As the muscle was taken from the lateral aspects of the donor trunk myotomes, it was unlikely that any cartilaginous cells were included. Following a 14-day healing period, the tail was amputated so as to transect the deplanted spinal cord and muscle. In these preparations two distinct axial systems regenerated. The cartilaginous structures stemming from the regenerating graft were identical with those found in all regenerating tails. These experiments demonstrate not only the irrelevance of the stump notochord to the cartilages in the tail but also that the cartilages form *de novo*.

c) *Induction of vertebral cartilages.*—The demonstration that in salamander embryos (Holtzer and Detwiler, 1953) the embryonic spinal cord activates somitic chondrogenesis was confirmed for the chick (Strudel, 1953; Watterson, Fowler, and Fowler, 1954) and for the mouse (Grobstein and Parker, 1954; Grobstein and Holtzer, 1955).

Thus in all major classes of vertebrates the spinal cord is active in transforming somite cells into cartilage cells of the embryonic vertebrae.

The following experiments established the same inductive interactions between spinal cord and trunk mesodermal cells in the regenerating tail of the larval salamander. A 3-mm. length of spinal cord from a larval salamander grafted into the right or left muscle mass of the tail induced supernumerary cartilaginous centra along the motor surface of the ectopic graft (S. Holtzer, 1956). These experiments did not involve amputation of the tail and so demonstrated that even in larval stages the spinal cord may transform cells in the differentiated muscle masses into vertebral cartilage cells. The muscle surrounding the grafted spinal cord underwent hyperplasia and was reorganized to form a bilateral mass centered about the graft.

d) Axiation of trunk mesodermal structures.—In addition to demonstrating the transformation of prospective myotomal cells into cartilage, the embryonic induction experiments of Holtzer and Detwiler (1953) suggested that the spinal cord plays a role in the axiation of the trunk tissues. Heterotopic grafts of tail-bud spinal cord into the somites of similarly aged hosts resulted in a reorganization and hyperplasia of the myotomal tissue and the formation of a second dorsal fin. Bilateral myotomal masses oriented around the grafted spinal cord formed from what normally would have produced a single unilateral myotome. Comparable results have been obtained with chick embryonic material (Avery, Chow, and Holtzer, 1956).

The following experiments demonstrated that in a similar manner the regenerating spinal cord influences the axiation of the tail tissues. The spinal cord was removed from its mid-line location and grafted into the right or left tail muscle mass. Two weeks later the tail was amputated. The regenerated tails in this series differed from those described earlier in only two details: (1) the cartilaginous centra did not abut on the stump of the notochord but arose within the muscle of the stump, and (2) the medial axis of the regenerated tail deviated from the medial axis of the host to the same extent that the regenerated spinal cord deviated from the mid-line of the host. In these experiments cartilaginous vertebrae were induced along that region of the spinal cord anterior to the level of amputation, as well as in the regenerate. In another series a piece of spinal cord, 6 segments long, was deviated dorsally to protrude into the dorsal fin. The dorsal muscle masses were injured at the same time. Within a few weeks a supernumerary tail was induced (Fig. 2), the long axis of which formed an acute angle with the long axis of the host. Morphologically, the structures of the induced tails were identical with those of a typical regenerated tail. The bilateral muscle masses surrounded the regenerated spinal cord, and ventral to the cord were the cartilaginous centra. Proximally, the cartilaginous structures were associated with neither the notochord nor the vertebrae of the host. Similarly, deviating the spinal cord at right angles to the A-P axis of the host resulted in a regenerated tail, the A-P axis of which was at right angles to that of the host. In this latter series, however, regeneration was not so extensive as when the spinal cord was deflected dorsally. These experiments involving deviation of the spinal cord demonstrated that the A-P axis of the mesodermal structures and the bilateral symmetry of the muscle are related to the direction of outgrowth of the regenerating spinal cord.

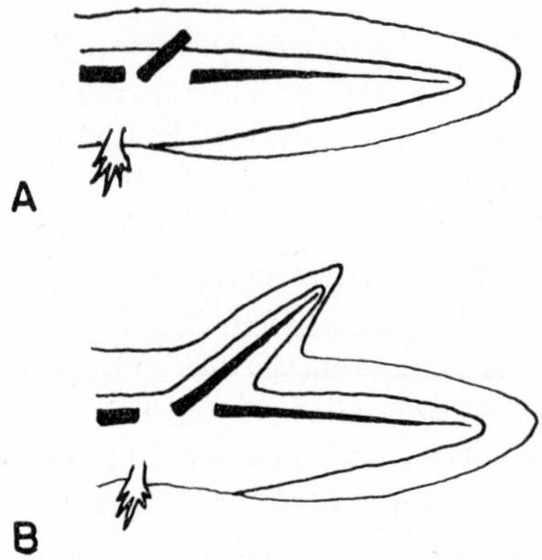

FIG. 2.—A piece of spinal cord six segments long was deflected dorsally, as shown in *A*. The tail in this preparation was not amputated. Within a month a supernumerary tail developed, as diagramed in *B*. These supernumerary tails are similar in all morphologic and histologic details to normal regenerated tails.

e) Localization and transmissibility of the cartilage-promoting activity and the morphogenetic role of the spinal cord.—Further analysis of the embryonic inductive relationship between spinal cord and somite cells revealed that (1) the cartilage-promoting action is confined primarily to the motor half of the spinal cord and (2) the cartilage-promoting factor is transmissible, i.e., the interaction is not dependent upon contact of the neural tissue with those somite cells which eventually form cartilage. Evidence for the localization of the cartilage-promoting activity to the motor half of the embryonic salamander, mouse, and chick spinal cord may be found in the respective papers of Holtzer (1951), Grobstein and Holtzer (1956), and Lash, Holtzer, and Holtzer (1957). That, in embryogenesis, vertebral cartilage forms at a distance from the surface of the neural tissue has been stressed (Holtzer, 1952*b*). Grobstein and Holtzer (1956) demonstrated the passage of the cartilage-promoting activity through a sheet of cells in tissue cultures with mouse material. Lash, Holtzer, and Holtzer (1957) have observed a transfilter effect with chick material in vitro. In addition, the latter workers report activity through a thin agar film.

The following experiments demonstrated not only that the ventral half of the regenerating spinal cord is unique with respect to its cartilage-promoting activity but that the spinal cord exerts a morphogenetic influence on the orientation of the individual vertebrae. Both these actions are effected by a factor which is transmissible through the intervening mesenchymal matrix. A 3-mm. length of larval spinal cord was removed, rotated 180° around its long axis, and grafted orthotopically. Following a 14-day healing period, the tail was amputated. In these animals the motor surface of the spinal cord lay dorsad, the sensory surface ventrad. Typical cartilaginous centra formed along the dorsal surface of the rotated spinal cord. Neural arches girdled the inverted spinal cord from the true motor surface to the true sensory surface. In short, centra formed along the geometrically dorsal surface of the spinal cord, and the neural arches developed in a dorsoventral direction. With respect to the spinal cord, the vertebrae were properly oriented, but, with respect to the rest of the animal, they were upside down. Thus not only is the spinal cord active histogenetically in the induction of cartilage cells, but presumably because of subtle biochemical differentials, it orders the architecture of the cartilaginous structures as well (see Holtzer, 1952*b*, and Grobstein, 1956, for additional evidence of differentials in the motor and ventral halves of the spinal cord).

MYOGENESIS IN TAIL REGENERATION AND IN THE EMBRYO

Little is known of the embryonic conditions initiating or maintaining the differentiation and growth of somitic muscle. The contention of Smithberg (1955) and others that the notochord is essential to embryonic myogenesis could not be confirmed. Recent work would indicate that the embryonic spinal cord stimulates the *growth* of salamander and chick muscle. Clusters of tail-bud salamander somites introduced into the dorsal fin of young larvae differentiated into small bundles of muscle. Similar grafts of somites plus notochord formed little more muscle than those cases of somites alone. In contrast, the same clusters of somites plus spinal cord resulted in the formation of large masses of muscle, much as if the somites had been left *in situ*. Intrafin grafts of somites plus forebrain, mesonephros, or liver produced no more muscle than somites alone or somites plus notochord (Holtzer and Detwiler, 1954; Holtzer, Lash, and Holtzer, 1956). Identical results have been obtained with chorio-allantoic grafts of chick material. Stimulation of muscle growth by the embryonic spinal cord is believed not to be mediated by peripheral nerves (Avery, Chow, and Holtzer, 1956; Holtzer and Avery, 1958).

It is perhaps significant that our knowledge of the factors conditioning the differentiation and growth of muscle in regeneration is correspondingly fragmentary. Recent experiments (S. Holtzer, 1954, 1956) tend to indicate that simple transformation of tail blastema cells into muscle cells is improbable. For example, if the muscle mass of the tail were reduced unilaterally, the corresponding muscle mass in the regenerate reflected the deficiency. As the mesenchymal blastema was bilateral in these experiments, the results are difficult to harmonize with the concept that blastema cells form muscle directly and independently of extra-blastemal influences (see Holtzer, Avery, and Holtzer, 1954, for comparable results with regenerating salamander limbs).

Though the earliest cellular interactions conditioning muscle differentiation are obscure, there is a striking similarity in the maturation of muscle from the myoblast stage onward in the mouse, chick, and salamander embryos and in the regenerating salamander tail. The intracellular distribution of muscle antigens in mature, embryonic, and regenerating muscle was determined by the fluorescein-labeled antibody technique (Coons *et al.*, 1942, 1950; Marshall, 1952, 1955). Adult chick myosin, prepared by the method of Mommaerts and Parrish, was injected into rabbits. The resulting antibodies were conjugated with fluorescein isocyanate. When glycerol-extracted adult chick muscle is "stained" with the labeled antibodies and visualized under the fluorescence microscope, a brilliant green fluorescence, indicating the binding of antibody, is localized in the A band (Holtzer, Marshall, and Finck, 1957). A similar cytologic picture is observed when adult mouse, rabbit, or salamander muscle is stained with the same labeled antibody. Glycerol-extracted kidney, liver, connective, or neural tissue do not bind the fluorescent reagent. Glycerol-extracted muscle fibers stained with the antiserum fail to contract when exposed to ATP (0.25 per cent in Simms solution, pH 6.8). Control fibers stained with labeled normal globulin contract vigorously. It is concluded that (1) an antigen or antigens localized in the area of the A band of chick, mouse, rabbit, and salamander muscle are related, at least to the extent of producing cross-reactions with rabbit antibodies produced against adult chick myosin and (2) ATP-induced contractions are inhibited when such antibodies are precipitated on the A band of glycerol-extracted fibers.

Myogenesis in the regenerating salamander tail was followed with the same labeled antibody as that used to stain the mature chick, mouse, rabbit, and salamander muscle. Glycerol-extracted regenerating tails were stained as whole mounts and then either teased or imbedded and sectioned at 1 μ. By comparing antibody-stained material under the fluorescence and phase-contrast microscopes, the following picture of myogenesis was arrived at: By the twelfth day, many mononucleated myoblasts have invaded the anterior portion of the regenerating tail. A single teased whole myoblast of this stage is seen in Figure 3. The richly vacuolated sarcoplasm and prominent pseudopodial extensions of the myoblast observed under phase are not seen under the fluorescence microscope, for these areas do not combine with the antibody to any

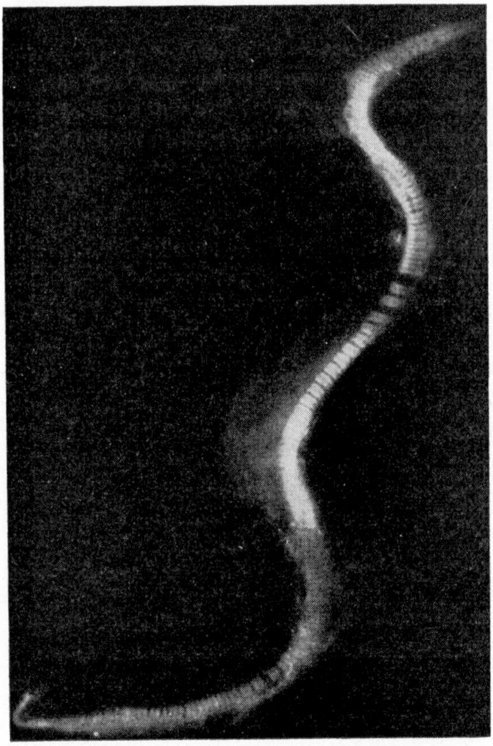

FIG. 3.—A single myoblast from an 11-day regenerating salamander tail. This myoblast was extracted with glycerol, stained with the fluorescein-labeled antimyosin antibody, and viewed under the fluorescence microscope. Note the prominent staining of the A bands. The sarcoplasm, nucleus, and I band do not bind the stain. Control myoblasts treated with normal labeled globulin do not exhibit A-band staining. Such controls contract vigorously when exposed to ATP, whereas myoblasts stained with the antimyosin antibody do not contract when exposed to ATP.

detectable extent. The cross-striated myofibrillar ribbon appears to be associated with the sarcolemma. Note the greater fluorescence along the lateral edges of the A band and the less intense staining of the H zone. The I and Z bands do not combine with the antibody. The size of the individual sarcomeres, even at this early stage, is of the same order of magnitude as that found in mature salamander muscle. Contraction bands are formed when these mononucleated myoblasts are exposed to ATP. These contraction bands induced by ATP are indistinguishable from similarly induced contraction bands in adult salamander, rabbit, mouse, or chick muscle. The contracted embryonic myofibrils are always parallel to one another. When stained with antibody, mononucleated regenerating myoblasts will not contract when exposed to ATP. Only muscle cells in the regenerating tail stain with the antibody (however, see Ebert, 1953).

Subsequent maturation involves the lateral extension of the myofibrillar sheet and the fusion of mononucleated myoblasts to form the multinucleated myotube. As the myoblast grows, the myofibrillar material extends as a thin sheet around the periphery of the cell. This lateral expansion of the cross-striated sheet appears to be appositional, for the different bands appear in register. That is to say, A band material adds to the A band, I bands add to I bands, etc. Given the adult size of the early sarcomere, elongation of the myofibril probably occurs by the addition of new sarcomeres at the ends of the fibril.

By the fifteenth or sixteenth day, bi- and trinucleated cells are present in the proximal areas of the regenerated tail. Distally, only mononucleated myoblasts of the kind described above are found. The cross-striated myofibrillar material in the early multinucleated muscle cells is disposed as a thin sheet around the central core of sarcoplasm. The nuclei are located in the core of the fiber.

The manner in which muscle nuclei increase in number is still uncertain. The absence of mitotic figures in multinucleated embryonic salamander muscle (Holtzer and Detwiler, 1953) and in regenerating mature mouse muscle (Lash, Holtzer, and Swift, 1956) has been stressed. Likewise, in regenerating salamander muscle mitotic figures have not been observed *within* the multinucleated muscle fibers. Mitotic figures are observed in mononucleated cells interspersed with maturing myotubes. In teased material, cases suggestive of the incorporation or fusion of mononucleated cells into multinucleated fibers have been found. When ATP-induced contractions of the myotubes are observed under phase, the regular contour of the vesicular muscle nuclei may be considerably distorted by the contracting myofibrils. The conspicuous infolding in both embryonic and regenerating muscle nuclei may have been misinterpreted as amitotic divisions. Evidence for fusion of chick myoblasts into multinucleated myotubes has been presented elsewhere (Holtzer, Abbott, and Lash, 1958).

SUMMARY

The foregoing account has deliberately emphasized the common histogenetic and morphogenetic activities involved in the formation of the axial structures in all vertebrates. This treatment has resulted in the omission of much data indicating that there are differences in aspects of the development of the axial structures in different vertebrates. Nevertheless, we feel these omissions to be justified on the grounds that all too frequently the basic unity of developmental mechanisms is lost sight of. If the concept of homology is to have any genetic meaning, it can only be in terms of common developmental mechanisms.

DISCUSSION

Discussion leader: A. STEFANELLI, *Institute of Comparative Anatomy, University of Rome*

DR. STEFANELLI introduced the discussion period by remarking that the problem of tail regeneration in amphibians, as well as that of lizards, is a very old one but continues to be of great interest, since tail regeneration is the most complete regenerative process occurring in vertebrates, including as it does the reconstitution of the entire axial system. And, as with all the old biological problems, it becomes a new problem when it is approached from a new point of view or with new techniques.

We know that regeneration does not repeat the morphogenetic processes of ontogenesis, but there is much evidence, and Dr. Holtzer has emphasized it, of similarity between embryogenesis and regeneration if we descend to the cellular level and compare induction, organization, and differentiation in both phenomena.

Of particular interest to DR. STEFANELLI is the finding of Dr. Holtzer that the spinal cord induces the vertebral cartilage and that only the motor half of the spinal cord has this power. The basic similarity in the cellular activities in the regenerating salamander axial system and the embryogenesis of the axial system of birds is seen in muscles treated with fluorescent myosin antibodies. This method seems to be very useful for following the precocious formation of myofibrils in myoblasts, the segregation of the myosin in the anisotropic band, and the shifts in the distribution of myosin, depending upon the degree of the contraction and the responsiveness of the early myoblast to ATP.

DR. STEFANELLI mentioned that he had very recently had an opportunity of observing in urodeles the failure of the notochord to regenerate, not only in larval stages, but also in embryonic stages up to the tail bud. This behavior is in sharp contrast with that of the anurans. It is paradoxical that the anurans, with a well-known reduced regenerative capacity as compared to that of urodeles, have the ability to regenerate an organ that fails to regenerate in urodeles. The regeneration of notochord is very active in embryonic and larval stages, as Dr. Stefanelli has observed, and can undergo hyperregeneration, owing to the difficulty of fusion of the newly produced chordal buds. Many cases of hyperregeneration of the tail of anuran tadpoles are caused by the hyperregeneration of the notochord and not by the direct influence of the activity of spinal cord, which is so clearly shown in urodeles and lizards (Stefanelli and Thermes, 1950). The best example of this chordal action is observed if a segment 2–3 mm. wide, including notochord and spinal cord, is excised from the ventral side of the tail of a frog tadpole. The two bulblike extremities of the regenerating spinal cord fuse, but the two regenerating extremities of the notochord, instead of fusing, grow ventrally to create a double branching of the notochord. Around this appendix of the notochord, with no accompanying spinal cord, a new secondary tail is induced.

The different behavior of urodele and anuran notochord, concluded Dr. Stefanelli, is not paradoxical; it is easily explained if we take into account that in the tail of larval anurans, owing to its being only a larval structure, skeleton-building activity does not exist. So in this larval organ only larval systems can regenerate. In urodeles, on the contrary, tail regeneration involves a second step of morphogenesis—the formation of a permanent tail lacking a notochord but possessing vertebral cartilages. In the adult urodele tail the notochord is vestigial.

In the general discussion which followed Dr. Stefanelli's remarks, Dr. Brunst (Roswell Park Memorial Institute) expressed great interest in the morphogenesis of cartilage in tail regeneration. He described experiments in which he had suppressed tail regeneration in the axolotl by X-radiation; but in the adjacent basal areas of the tail, where the irradiation dosage was insufficient to prevent regeneration, a secondary tail was stimulated to form, which possessed a cartilaginous rod instead of a notochord. When, however, tail regeneration in anuran tadpoles is suppressed by X-radiation, the spinal cord grows out to great lengths, although no other tissues are regenerated.

Dr. Weiss (Rockefeller Institute) pointed out that it is important to make a distinction between the phenomenon of induction and its expression. The laying-down of ground substance and the differentiation of cartilage out of it may be the expression of the inductive stimulus of the spinal cord, and the space which is observed between the spinal cord and the cartilage may be secondarily produced as a result of the cartilage differentiation. He postulated, also, the possibility of there being a concentration gradient next to the neural tissue, the optimum concentration for chondrogenesis being at a distance from the neural tissue. Around the latter there might exist a zone of inhibition. Dr. Lash (University of Pennsylvania) commented that, both in vivo and in vitro, there is a discrete area of cellular material between the neural tissue and the cartilage. When the Chen culture method was used, one always obtained an area of mesenchyme-like cells between the neural tissue and the forming cartilage, but this intervening area varied from a layer of just a few cells to approximately half the diameter of the explanted neural tissue. If one chooses to think of this area as a zone of inhibition, it varies considerably, depending upon the culture conditions employed.

Dr. Balinski (University of Witwatersrand) inquired as to the source of the cells which form cartilage and whether these cells are inverted along with inversion of the spinal cord in Dr. Holtzer's experiments. Dr. Holtzer explained that the meninges were removed in reversing the spinal cord, and thus the possibility of including pro-cartilage cells in the operation was nil. He further mentioned that mitotic counts made by Mrs. Holtzer strongly suggest that the majority of cells in the blastema must go into the formation of cartilage. Muscle, on the other hand, is differentiated from mononucleated cells derived from muscle in the tail stump. He suggested the possibility that a similar situation might hold true for limb regeneration.

DR. MOSCONA (Hebrew University) asked whether Dr. Holtzer had actually obtained muscle nuclei free of cytoplasm. DR. HOLTZER emphasized that these nuclei were surrounded by a scanty film of cytoplasm.

DR. BUTLER (Princeton University) asked whether there was a size relationship between the ventral region of the spinal cord and the cartilaginous rod. DR. HOLTZER answered that no ratio between the volume of the neural tissue and the volume of the cartilaginous rod had been discovered. However, the circumference of the cartilaginous rod is remarkably similar to what the circumference of the notochord should be if it were there.

DR. WEISS then asked Dr. Stefanelli about the importance of the nervous system in the regeneration of the tail of the lizard. DR. STEFANELLI asserted that deviations in the spinal cord of the tail of the lizard directed new tail regeneration. DR. SINGER (Cornell University) agreed that, in his experience, the spinal cord was essential for tail regeneration in the lizard; and DR. HOLTZER added that salamander tail regeneration was similarly dependent on the spinal cord. DR. WEISS then referred to one of his early publications in which was described the transplantation of a tail blastema of a lizard to the limb region. The tail blastema differentiated into a good tail with segmented muscles, scales, and other structures of tail type. He emphasized that no spinal cord tissue was present in these tail regenerates.

DR. CHALKLEY (National Cancer Institute) inquired as to the relationship between the old muscle of the stump and the regenerating muscle of the blastema. DR. HOLTZER described the myoblasts which are found in close association with the muscle fibers of the tail stump. As such, they are actually first detectable anterior to the level of transection. Whether the myoblasts are directly derived from the muscle of the stump or from the mesenchymal blastemal cells cannot be critically determined with the methods used. Circumstantial evidence leads him to favor the notion that they are not derived from the blastemal cells. He feels that comments to the effect that muscle cells are "more highly differentiated" than connective tissue cells lack experimental verification and contribute nothing to further causal analysis. Mitotic figures are found among prospective mononucleated muscle cells. Mitotic figures have not been observed in multinucleated, cross-striated muscle fibers. Later, clusters of mononucleated myoblasts have their nuclei so aligned as to suggest incipient segmentation of the future tail muscles. The differentiated regenerated muscle fibers are grouped into distinct, though irregular, segments.

ADDENDUM

If, under any circumstances, a tail-like structure can regenerate with segmented vertebral cartilages and muscles, though the spinal cord is completely absent, then much of the foregoing would have to be reinterpreted. Therefore, the reports of Trampusch (this symposium) and of Glade (1958) that regenerated segmented vertebrae and muscles can be obtained in the absence of spinal cord require some comment. It is surprisingly difficult to set up a large number of operated animals grafting *just* vertebral cartilages or just muscle or just skin from the tail of an adult salamander into a limb. Dr. Trampusch was kind enough to review some of his slides with me, and it was found that in cases where the original graft was intended to consist just of vertebral cartilage, appreciable masses of central nervous tissue and segmented muscle were inadvertently included. Similarly, grafts of muscle included bits of cartilage, central nervous tissue, etc. It is worth recalling that exceedingly small masses of trunk muscle, when grafted ectopically with a fragment of neural tissue, will regenerate segmented cartilages and muscles (S. Holtzer, 1956).

A 30-day regenerated larval tail consists of approximately 20 segmented vertebrae and perhaps 15 clearly defined segmented muscle masses. The regenerated tail may be over fifteen to twenty times the length of a regenerated lower arm. Now Woronzowa (1939) and Liosner (1941) and others have grafted pieces of trunk muscle into normal and irradiated limbs and have observed that, following amputation of the limb in a few cases, the regenerate possesses, in addition to limb elements, one or two irregular masses of vertebral cartilage and some trunk muscle. This chimeric structure is rarely longer than a regenerated limb, and all the tissues are highly disorganized. Is this to be construed as showing that trunk muscle can, by itself, regenerate a tail? We think not, for the following reasons: (1) one or two pieces of vertebral cartilage or segmented muscle do not make a regenerated tail; (2) small nodules of vertebral cartilage may have been included with the muscle, which, when grafted to the limb, grew in size; (3) after removing the spinal cord and amputating the tail, though a tail does not regenerate, an irregular mound of vertebral cartilage does form at the amputated surface (Holtzer, Holtzer, and Avery, 1955, p. 159); and (4) masses of muscle introduced into the dorsal fin, followed by amputation of the tail through the grafted muscle, does not regenerate strings of cartilaginous vertebrae, as it will if a piece of spinal cord is present (S. Holtzer, 1956).

Glade (1958) states that salamander limbs ensheathed with tail skin and then amputated will regenerate tail structures. He interprets his results as indicating that tail skin organizes the mesodermal tissues of the regenerating limb into tail vertebral cartilages and muscles. Again, if Glade's findings are substantiated and the organ-determining activity of the skin unequivocally demonstrated, then our own contention of the role of the spinal cord in tail regeneration will have to be revised.

The following experiments, however, not only fail to confirm the organ-determining capacity of skin in a regenerating limb or tail but serve to emphasize some of the difficulties associated with this type of experiment (Holtzer, 1958). Rectangular pieces of skin from larval salamanders were stripped from the flank or dorsal fin of the body or tail. Each strip was cut in two. One piece of skin was grafted to a forelimb whose own skin had been removed; the other piece was fixed, sectioned, and stained to determine whether trunk muscle or cartilage cells were adhering to the skin. Skin from the body or tail flank did not contain significant amounts of muscle or cartilage, though connective tissue cells were present in patches. In contrast, skin from the dorsal fin, either body or tail, revealed large masses of adhering connective tissue. Limbs wrapped in flank or dorsal fin skin were amputated above the elbow. Of 16 cases in which the skin graft took, 3 failed to regenerate, 3 formed abnormal regenerates of a distinct limb nature, whereas 5 regenerated respectable limbs. The salient characteristics of the remaining 5 cases were their gross finlike appearance and irregular epidermal projections. Sections of these 5 cases revealed the finlike appearance to be due solely to much loose connective tissue, similar to the cell-sparse connective tissue of the dorsal fin. The cores of the epidermal spikes likewise consisted of connective tissue. Of particular interest is the fact that, though the cartilages and muscles in these 5 cases were malformed, nothing in their shape or distribution even remotely suggested tail structures. The fact that 4 of the 5 "finlike" regenerates were obtained from limbs covered with dorsal fin skin and the fact that such skin has many fin connective tissue cells adhering to it suggest that the finlike appearance is due to fin connective tissue inadvertently included with the original graft (see also Newth, 1958; Holtzer, Avery, and Holtzer, 1954).

In the complementary series larval tails were prepared with patches of larval limb skin. Histologic examination of limb skin used for grafting indicated that the grafts were free of underlying cartilage or muscle, though connective tissue cells were present. The limb skin graft took on 9 animals and the tails amputated through the graft. In 5 cases a typical tail regenerated, in 3 cases the tail was malformed, and 1 case failed to regenerate.

This type of operation cannot readily be performed on *adult* salamanders. Of 20 pieces of tail skin from adult salamanders large enough to envelop the limb, 14 saved for histologic inspection exhibited large masses of tail muscle, and in 8 of these cases nodules of vertebral or ventral rib cartilages were present. In short, when in a small percentage of operated animals an adult limb covered with adult tail "skin" regenerates a tail-like structure, it is impossible to determine which structures were included with, or derived from, the grafted "skin" and which regenerated from the limb tissues. Indeed, the low frequency of such cases in Glade's report and the limited size of the outgrowth itself are, we believe, reasonable evidence that limb tissues are incapable of being transformed into tail structures. It should be borne in mind that a regenerated tail is many times the length of a regenerated limb. A further complication in this system is that abortive limb regenerates often terminate in a single cartilaginous digit or spike; the alignment of carpals and metacarpals in these digits or spikes may readily be mistaken for segmented vertebrae.

In this connection it is worth noting that Dr. C. Thornton, who has made a more exhaustive analysis of this problem, has also concluded that the salamander skin does not determine the nature of the underlying mesodermal structures during regeneration (personal communication). And, finally, the ectoderm-mesoderm relationship in the developing limb of the chick embryo likewise denies an organ-determining role to the epidermis. When wing, leg, or tail epidermis is grafted to ectopic sites, it does not mobilize the underlying mesodermal tissues to develop corresponding structures (Zwilling, 1955).

Origin of blastema cells.—What tissue or tissues contribute cells to the formation of the regenerated tail? More specifically, what cells form the regenerated vertebral cartilages and muscles? Evidence has been presented elsewhere that the notochord and fin connective tissue are not involved (Holtzer, Avery, and Holtzer, 1956; Newth, 1958); and though the evidence is not critical, it is improbable that the spinal cord supplies cells which eventually differentiate into cartilage or muscle. Of the three remaining stump tissues—cartilage, muscle, and connective tissue associated with muscle—there is unequivocal evidence that cartilage *need* not be the major source of blastema cells. For example: (1) 10 days after amputating the tail of a salamander embryo (stage 38, Harrison's stages), cartilaginous centra will appear in the regenerating tail. At this early stage in development the forelimbs have just begun chondrifying, and vertebral cartilages have not developed, even in the brachial areas. Thus the precocious cartilages of the regenerating embryonic tail could not have been derived from cartilage cells in the stump (Holtzer, unpublished observations). (2) Larval trunk muscle without nodules of cartilage, plus a piece of spinal cord, can be introduced into the tail dorsal fin. When the tail of the host is transected through the graft, a tail regenerates from the host and the graft. Both tails consist of segmented cartilages and muscle. These two types of experiments clearly indicate that cartilage and muscle in the regenerated tail are not dependent upon the presence of cartilage in the stump.

This leaves two tissues as the only source of cells for the regeneration blastema—muscle and its associated connective tissues. Circumstantial evidence favoring muscle as the major source of cells for the blastema can be summarized as follows: Both in vitro and in vivo experiments indicate that the multinucleated muscle fibers of the chick and mouse may be fragmented into mononucleated cells, which then divide and may reform multinucleated muscle fibers (Holtzer, Abbott, and Lash, 1958; Lash, Holtzer, and Swift, 1957). When multinucleated fibers are fragmented or damaged, the myofibrils undergo dissolution and myosin is released into the cytoplasm (Holtzer, Abbott, and Cavanaugh, 1959). In uninjured muscle cells, myosin is never found in the cytoplasm but is exclusively localized in the A band of the myofibrils (Holtzer, Marshall, and Finck, 1957). It is of interest, then, to note that many early blastema cells of the limb or tail exhibit solubilized myosin throughout their cytoplasm (Holtzer, unpublished observations). We are currently testing the notion that blastema cells are the mononucleated cells derived from muscle fibers injured at the time of amputation and that, in the tail at least, some of these cells are transformed into cartilage by the action of the spinal cord.

· III ·

The Cellular Basis of Limb Regeneration

D. T. CHALKLEY[1]

Department of Biology, University of Notre Dame

Regeneration, like other biologic processes, is susceptible of analysis at various levels of organization. While an attack on the fundamentals of the process should unquestionably begin at or near the molecular level and progress to more complex supramolecular situations, the absence of adequate methods compels us, instead, to move down the historical avenue of approach dealing with superficially more simple natural units—the cells and tissues. The knowledge gained in such studies is basic only to an understanding of tissue and organ development and cannot provide information as to the more fundamental processes of regeneration. However, any study of the physiology and biochemistry of regeneration will benefit from a clear statement of the morphologic events of the process. Physiologists, particularly those who are much impressed by the amazing uniformity of intermediary metabolic processes in various cell processes, frequently need to be reminded of the complexity of morphogenetic processes. A brei presents a very satisfyingly homogeneous appearance, even when prepared from an extremely non-homogeneous tissue source such as an embryo. It is desirable to emphasize that in morphogenetically active tissues this morphologic non-homogeneity may be paralleled by physiologic non-homogeneity.

This chapter of the symposium reviews the present state of our knowledge of the cellular basis of regeneration and its possible interpretation in terms of cell migration and of the possible changes in the states of differentiation of the participant cells at various stages of the process.

Except for differences in extent, the events which follow amputation of the amphibian limb appear to be identical with those following amputation of the tail. The soft tissues contract over a somewhat greater distance in the limb because of the increased length of the muscle fibers. A

[1] Present address: Division of Research Grants, National Institutes of Health, Bethesda, Maryland.

clot is rapidly formed over the amputation surface, and the adjacent epithelium begins to migrate over the wound within 15–45 minutes (Lash, 1955). The process appears to be complete within 24 hours or less. This migration is not associated with local epidermal cell division, nor, for that matter, are mitoses found at any level of the stump during the first 12 hours (Inoue, 1954). A similar mesenchymal migration occurs beneath the wound surface as dissociated cells, emerging from the stump tissues, accumulate between the wound epithelium and the subjacent sub-epithelial formed tissues. This immigration continues for at least 72 hours, even in the presence of antimitotic agents. Colchicine (Luscher, 1946), nitrogen mustard (Skowron and Roguski, 1953), and aminoketones (Dettelbach, 1952) have no effect on this process. Further accumulation of cells is blocked by these inhibitors, but, interestingly enough, there is no detectable mitotic activity in the tissues adjacent to the amputation surface on which these inhibitors might be presumed to act. Thus Litwiller (1939) reported an accumulation of the order of 9,000 cells during the first 15 days of regeneration (Fig. 1) in the complete absence of mitosis (Fig. 2). Bassina (1940) reported blastemata averaging 15,000 cells which were formed in less than 6 days (Fig. 1) and also in the complete absence of mitoses (Fig. 2). Rose (1948) found an accumulation of only 375 cells (Fig. 1) in the complete absence of mitoses but noted the addition of another 18,300 cells between his "epithelial mound" and "early blastema" stages accompanied by a mitotic index of 1.4 per cent. Assuming that the interval between these stages is not more than 48 hours, as indicated by the chronological ages of the examples cited by Rose, and applying the compound-interest formula to the initial accumulation, we find that a total of 164 division intervals would be necessary to produce the required number of cells. This allows only 18 minutes per division, while observed times are appreciably higher. The only observations on amphibian cell division in vivo are those of Clark (1912), who found frog epidermal mitoses to last 263 minutes. Observations in vitro on frog and newt fibroblasts indicate times of from 83 to 93 minutes. Computations by Luscher (1946), employing the colchicine method, indicate an in vivo division time of 99–104 minutes for tail mesenchyme cells.

The inadequacy of the observed mitotic activity in the early blastema to account for the growth of that tissue had been generally recognized before Rose's documentation of the phenomenon. Various theories have been put forward to explain it. The oldest of these theories is that of a hematogenic origin of the blastema cells, presumably from extravasated leukocytes. First proposed by Colucci (1884), contributions of varying magnitude from this source have been described by Hellmich (1930), Kazancev (1934), and Ide-Rozas (1936). Any idea that such a contribution was in any way critical was disposed of by a series of experiments by Butler (1935), Brunst and Chérémetiéva (1936), and Butler and O'Brien (1942). These authors alternately shielded and exposed restricted sites on a large number of amphibians to X-rays and demonstrated that regeneration invariably followed amputation through a

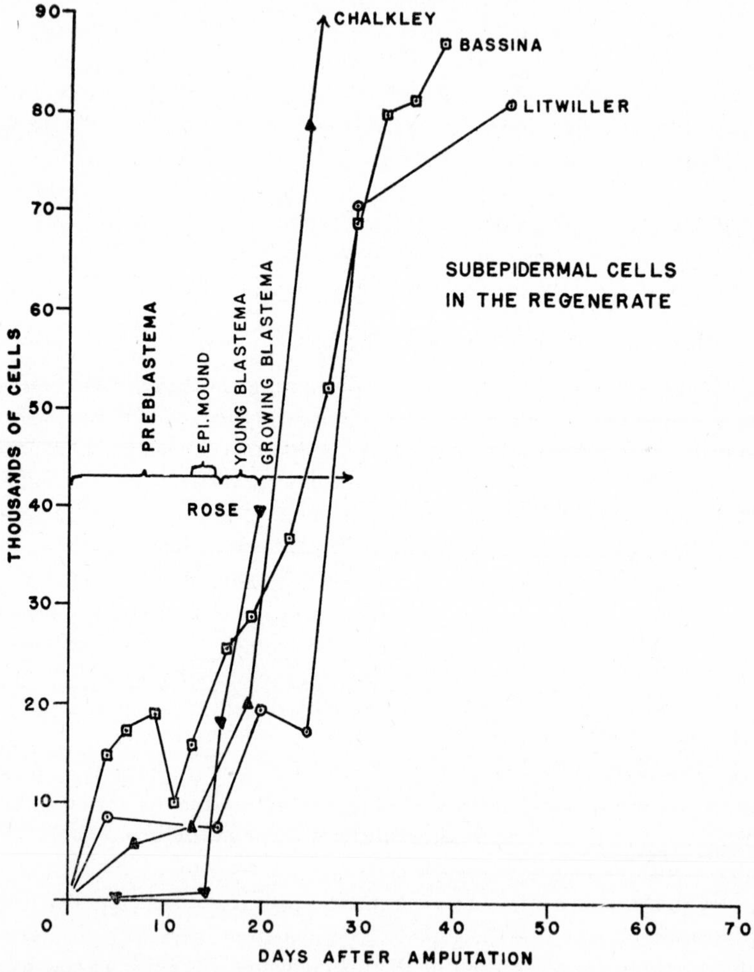

FIG. 1.—Numbers of cells in the regenerate at various dates after amputation (Bassina, Chalkley, Litwiller) or during various stages of regeneration (Rose). The chronological spread and degrees of overlap of the stages are not necessarily accurate but reflect the ages of the specimens assigned to the various stages by Rose (1948).

shielded zone, even if all other portions of the organism had been exposed. Regeneration failed with equal invariability if the amputation plane passed through even a small irradiated zone in an otherwise intact animal. Butler and O'Brien concluded that the cells of the blastema "have an exclusive and restricted origin at the site of the amputation."

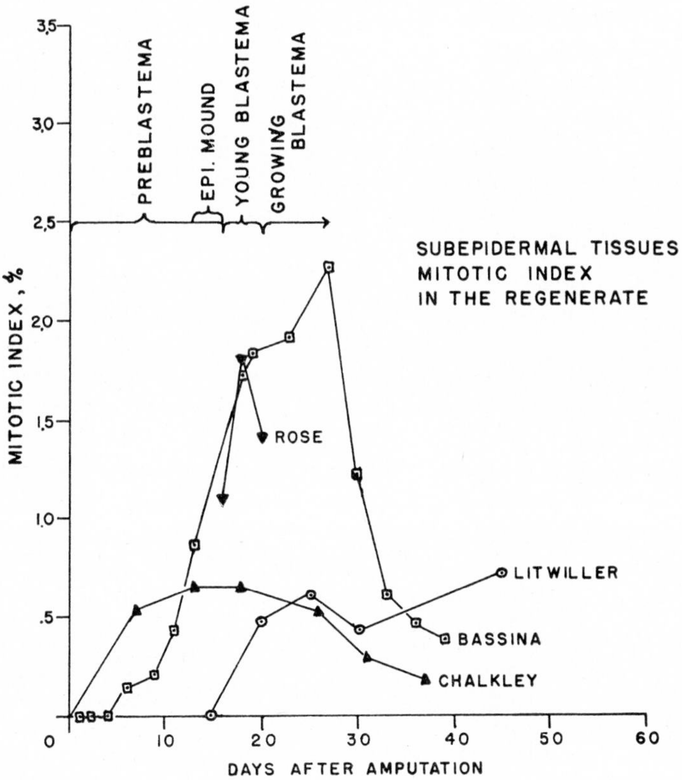

FIG. 2.—Mitotic index in the subepidermal tissues of the regenerate at various dates after amputation (Bassina, Chalkley, Litwiller) or during various stages of regeneration (Rose). The chronological spread and degrees of overlap of the stages are not necessarily accurate but reflect the ages of the specimens assigned to the various stages by Rose (1948).

An amitotic origin of the early blastema was first proposed by Towle (1901) and later by Bassina (1940). The evidence in both instances was circumstantial. No descriptive or quantitative studies of the distribution of amitotic figures were undertaken. The mechanism was simply proposed as a last resort after all other possibilities had been considered and rejected. Several authors, including Kazancev (1934), Ide-Rozas

(1936), Mettetal (1939), and Polezhayev and Ginsburg (1942), have specifically denied the occurrence of amitoses.

Figures closely resembling the amitotic figures of certain protozoan macronuclei can be found in the blastema and stump tissues of *Triturus*. Their distribution does not show any correlation with increase in cell number in any part of the limb. The total number of such figures found at any one time does not exceed 0.6 per cent of the mitoses found at the same time in the same tissue. It seems highly probable that these are "pseudo-amitotic figures" produced by the constriction of the nuclei of cells or by the fragmentation of large polymorphic nuclei.

It has also been suggested that the critical mass of the definitive blastema is provided by the immigration of epidermal cells from the thickened late wound epithelium. This hypothesis was first advanced by Godlewski (1928) and has recently been revived by Rose (1948). There can be no question that the epidermal and subepidermal tissues are closely associated during the early period of blastema formation and become clearly separate only after the formation of a basement membrane between the two tissues. Frequently, large masses of epithelial cells protrude into the underlying blastema, and the boundary between the two tissues becomes progressively less distinct near the tip of the protrusion.

While Rose has interpreted these areas of intrusion and contact as indicative of the ingression of epidermal cells, Ide-Rozas (1936) has described them as areas of egression of cells from blastema to epidermis. I interpret them as areas of chance apposition of tissues of approximately equal cellular density along the borders of epidermal infoldings produced at the time of amputation. As a result of the rapid proliferative growth of the young blastema, the average size of the subepidermal cells decreases, the intercellular matrix formation fails to keep pace with cell division, and the number of subepidermal cells per unit volume of tissue rises to a value comparable with that of normal epidermis. At the same time, the epidermal cells lose their close-packed arrangement and become separated, bound together only by tenuous and poorly resolved intercellular bridges. The loss of these and other characteristic properties of the two tissues renders the line of demarcation between them indistinct. The impression of exchange between the tissues in such areas is easily obtained.

Rose has supported his interpretation of this phenomenon with measurements of cell numbers which show an abrupt drop in the number of epidermal cells from 43,900 in his "epidermal mound" stage to 27,600 in the "young blastema" stage. This is shown in Figure 3. Simultaneously, as shown in Figure 1, his counts of subepidermal cells show an increase of from 1,100 to 19,300 cells. The changes are almost compensatory, and the data, as presented, are statistically significant. Unfortunately, the corresponding data of Litwiller (1939), Bassina (1940), and Chalkley (1954) fail to indicate any such abrupt rise in the number of subepidermal cells or, with the exception of Bassina's data, any comparable drop in the number of cells in the overlying epidermis.

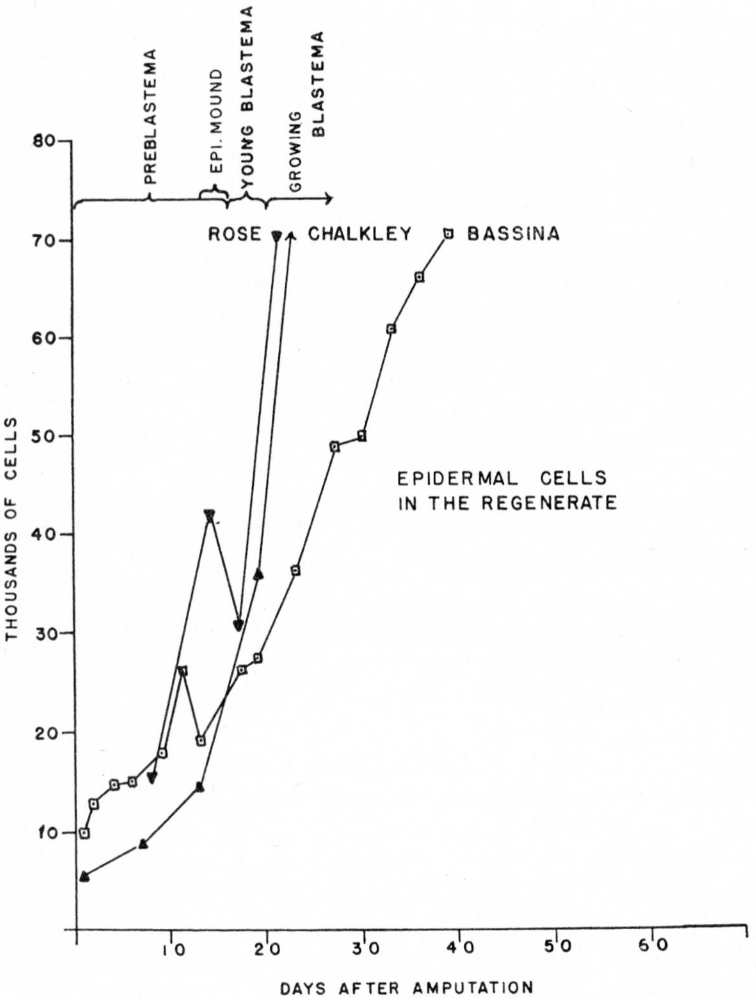

FIG. 3.—Numbers of epidermal cells in the regenerate at various dates after amputation (Bassina, Chalkley) or during various stages of regeneration (Rose). The chronological spread and degrees of overlap of the stages are not necessarily accurate but reflect the ages of the specimens assigned to the various stages by Rose (1948).

Strict comparison with Rose's data is hampered by his failure to refer them to a truly independent variable. He separated his limbs on the basis of histologic stages, which, he states, cannot be identified with distinct chronologic intervals. This is unfortunate because the identifications of the several stages are made in terms of histologic characteristics which conform to a previously conceived hypothesis. It is not surprising that quantification of these characteristics should produce data which support the hypothesis.

Fortunately, experimental studies also bear on this problem. Rose, Quastler, and Rose (1953) irradiated forelimbs with doses of as much as 10,000 r and then stripped the irradiated epidermis from the limbs, permitting the normal, unirradiated epidermis of the shoulder to migrate distally and re-cover the exposed subepidermal tissues. Following amputation, these limbs regenerated, though those receiving the highest dosages showed considerable delay. On the other hand, Fimian (1951) shielded the distal millimeter of recently amputated limbs and irradiated the shoulder region with 5,000 r. Regenerates appeared but failed to develop normally and regressed after a few days. Histologic examination of the limb tissues showed that epidermal mitoses were reduced even in the shielded epidermis but that a normal mitotic index, for that stage of the regenerative process, was attained by the eleventh day following amputation. Mitotic activity in the subepidermal tissues was completely suppressed in the exposed region until the eleventh day and, though it reappeared at that date, never reached a normal level thereafter. Thus in the presence of normal mitotic activity in a histologically normal wound epidermis, but of markedly reduced mitotic activity in the subepidermal tissues, regeneration proceeded aberrantly and ultimately halted. The observations of Rose *et al.* may be explained by the phenomenon described by Luther (1948) following distal irradiation of intact tails. He found that the replacement of the irradiated epidermal cells is followed by a similar replacement of the immediately subepidermal cells. It would appear highly probable that some viable subepidermal cells may have accompanied the replacement epithelium during the recovery of the stripped limbs. In Fimian's cases the replacement was necessarily slower, since the original epidermis remained in place. In such a case the accumulation of a sufficient mass of blastema cells was long delayed, and the inadequate accumulation blastema, formed only by dissociated and mitotically inactive cells, regressed.

The hypothesis of a definitive epidermal origin of the regeneration blastema is also not supported by the work of Heath (1953). He created tissue chimeras by exchanging epidermal and subepidermal limb-bud tissues between embryos with markedly different growth potentials. Both the chimeras and the regenerates formed by chimeras consisting of grafted epidermis and host subepidermis showed size characteristics of the host tissue. Regenerates formed by chimeras consisting of grafted subepidermal tissues and host epidermis occasionally showed some characteristics of the host limb.

The possibility of an epidermal contribution to the blastema remains, but the extent of such a contribution in normally developing regenerates must be slight and of no significance as far as the developmental characteristics of the subepidermal blastema are concerned.

The sole remaining possible source of blastema cells is the old stump. This is the source indicated by the great majority of descriptive studies. Reviews of the earlier literature have been presented by Mettetal (1939), Schotté (1939), and Weiss (1939). The former author attributes blastema formation solely to the proliferation of loose connective tissue elements. He specifically denies contributions by the two other distinct subepidermal tissues—muscle and cartilage. This view of a limited fibroblastic origin of the blastema has been supported recently by Manner (1953). Schotté, on the other hand, concluded that the blastema took origin from all the tissues of the limb—muscle, cartilage, and the ubiquitous connective tissues. Weiss attributes blastema origin to the local proliferation of still unidentified reserve cells, presumably associated with connective tissue elements.

In 1947 I began a quantitative histologic analysis of the histologic changes occurring during forelimb regeneration in *Triturus viridescens*. The object of these studies was to determine whether any correlation existed between the proliferation rates of the tissues of the old stump and the rates of appearance of new cells of the same tissues in the regenerate. This would provide evidence as to the identity and degree of contribution of all elements of the limb to the regenerate. As a matter of fact, a very close correlation of the type anticipated can be shown to exist. But it became quite evident during the course of the study that the difficulties inherent in cell identification during morphologic dedifferentiation and dissociation of the stump tissues and the impossibility of determining the physiologic state of a cell from the study of fixed tissues make it impossible to distinguish clearly between the three hypotheses mentioned above.

The data presented are drawn largely from Chalkley (1954) and from unpublished material collected in the same study. The animals used are not a haphazard sample. Three animals were sacrificed from the experimental group on each of seven dates. The over-all changes in stump and regenerate volumes of the three limbs, determined on the day prior to sacrifice, placed one of these three animals near the group mean and the other two near the values indicated by the group standard deviations.

As shown in Figure 4, the rate of accumulation of cells in the regenerating limbs (graph *L*) is essentially constant during the first 30 days after amputation. Initially, the bulk of this accumulation is confined to the stump (graph *S*), and it is not until the twenty-second day that it is transferred to the regenerate proper (graph *R*). The decrease in the stump accumulation, which is concomitant with the abrupt rise in the

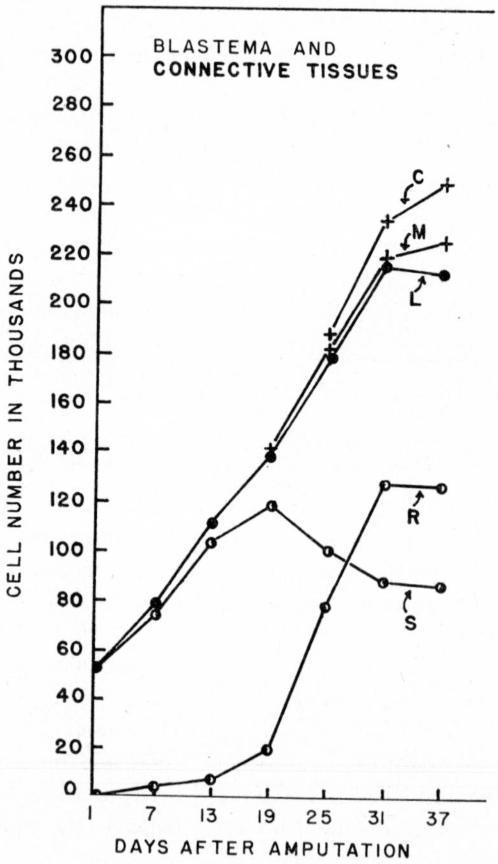

FIG. 4.—Changes in the numbers of blastema and connective tissue cells combined in the regenerating stump (*S*), in the regenerate proper (*R*), in the entire regenerating limb (*L*), and in the entire limb plus the redifferentiating muscle cells (*M*) and plus the redifferentiating cartilage cells (*C*). (From Chalkley, 1954.)

number of cells in the regenerate, strongly suggests a distal migration of cells from stump to regenerate.

The pattern of this migration is clearly indicated by the change in cell distribution along the limb axis. This is shown in Figure 5. Accumulation of cells occurs along the entire length of the stump and regenerate, though this accumulation centers about a peak which, as of the seventh day after amputation, is located some 0.56 mm. proximad from the amputation plane (indicated by the arrows). By the nineteenth day the accumulation in the stump is at a maximum. The increase has continued

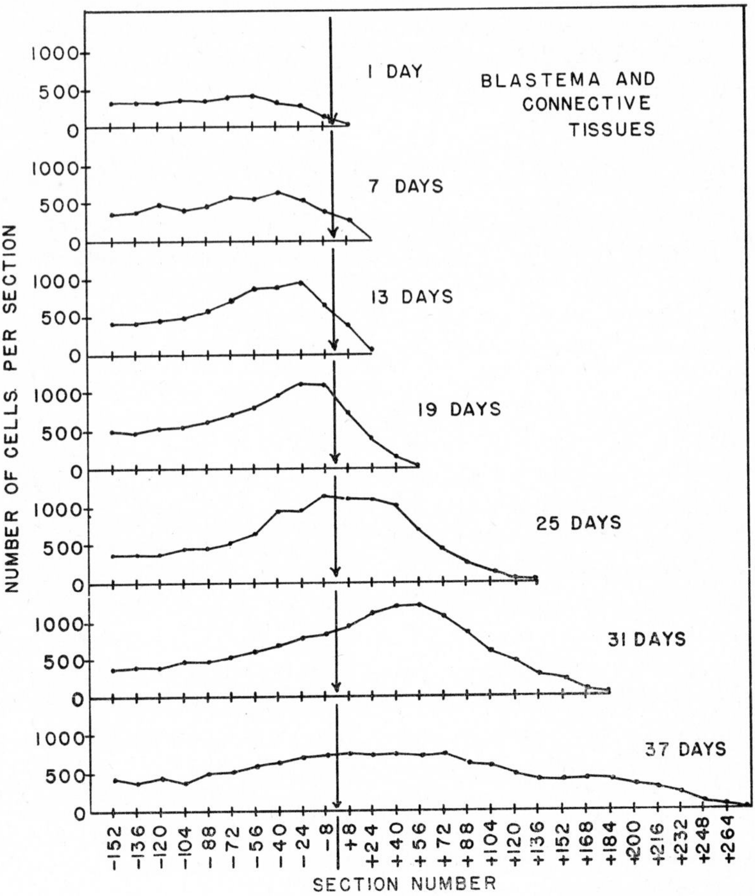

FIG. 5.—Changes in the distribution of blastema and connective tissue cells along the axis of the regenerating limb. Arrows indicate the amputation plane. (From Chalkley, 1954.)

along the entire limb axis, but the level of peak accumulation has moved distally and is now only 0.24 mm. proximad from the amputation plane. The peak then shifts into the regenerate, reaching a level 0.56 mm. from the amputation plane on the thirty-first day. The shift is real. Notice that the number of cells in the stump decreases along the entire length of the stump axis. There is no indication of a proximad migration and little or no necrosis.

Distal migration of a mitotically active zone, from stump to regenerate, accompanies the shift in numbers of cells. This is clearly shown in Figure 6. Only 2 per cent of the mitoses are found in the regenerate on the seventh day, though it contains 17 per cent of the blastema cells. By the nineteenth day the regenerate contains 29 per cent of the mitoses and 23 per cent of the blastema cells. Its continued growth is then essentially independent of mitotic activity and cell migration from the stump, though both these processes continue in diminishing degree for some time. Notice that the distribution of the mitotic index in Figure 6 suggests an "apical growth cone" such as that described by Holtzer, Holtzer, and Avery (1953) for the tail. A similar distribution of mitoses was described in *T. pyrrhogaster* by Litwiller (1939). The distribution of total mitoses is more or less normal and extends along much of the length of the blastema, with the largest number of the cells being added well back from the limb tip. Also notice that there is no interruption in any of the distributions at or near the amputation plane.

This evidence of early cellular migration is of particular interest in view of the demonstration by Singer (1955) of the existence of a barrier, or barriers, between the stump and regenerate as of the nineteenth day after amputation. This barrier resists the passage of micropipettes from stump to regenerate and the passage of infusates from regenerate to stump. Singer has suggested the existence of a coarse barrier, possibly consisting of a loose network of collagenous fibrils, occupying roughly the position of the amputation plane. Such a network could be felt but would be difficult, if not impossible, to detect microscopically with the ordinary histologic techniques used in most studies, including the present one. The barrier to infusates, Singer suggested, may be little more than a change in the amount of intercellular space available for rapid perfusion, or it may be no barrier at all in the physical sense but simply an increased vascular bed which rapidly removes perfusates from the distal stump. Measurements of available intercellular space and of vascular space, as shown in Figure 7, indicate no abrupt changes at or near the amputation plane. This leaves untested a third hypothetical barrier mechanism suggested by Singer—that the movement of edema fluids from stump to regenerate interferes with the basipetal movements of perfusates from regenerate to stump.

It seems reasonably well demonstrated that the major source of the cells of the forelimb regenerate in *T. viridescens* is the old stump and that there are three overlapping stages in the formation of the regenerate proper: (1) an initial distal migration of cells unaccompanied by cell

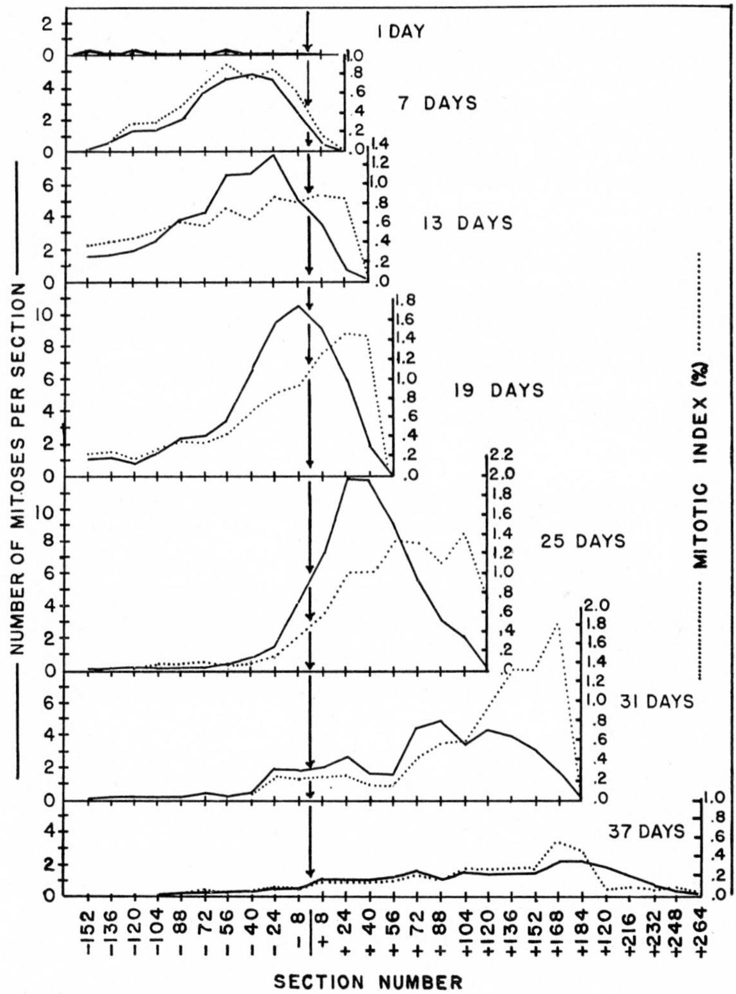

FIG. 6.—Changes in the distribution of the blastema and connective tissue cell mitoses and mitotic index along the axis of the regenerating limb. The index is expressed as per cent cells per section. Arrows indicate the amputation plane. (From Chalkley, 1954.)

division, a process which contributes, at most, a few thousand cells and which terminates within the first 3 or 4 days; (2) migration of mitotically produced cells from stump to regenerate, a process which begins some 4 days after amputation and produces a minimum of 60,000 cells; (3) continued division of these migratory cells in the regenerate proper. This produces a minimum of 100,000 additional cells.

I have repeatedly called attention to the absence of breaks in the distribution of cell counts or space measurements at or near the amputation plane. It is evident that a distinction between stump and regenerate is

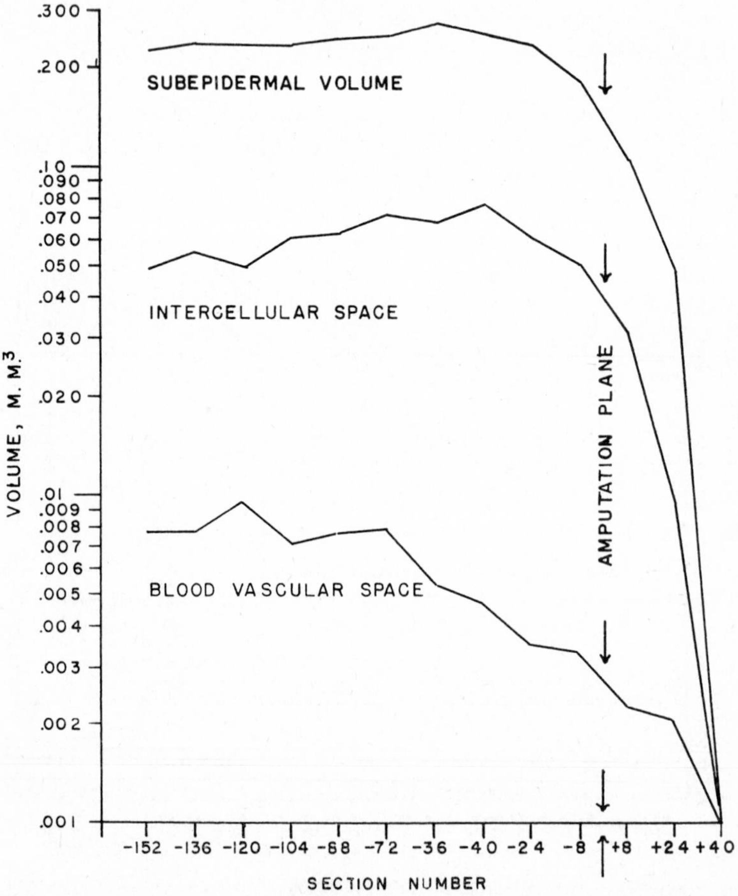

FIG. 7.—Changes in the distribution of total subepidermal volume, intercellular space and blood vascular space along the axis of the regenerating limb on the nineteenth day after amputation. Arrows indicate the amputation plane. Note that the volume scale is logarithmic.

completely arbitrary insofar as blastema cell production and migration are concerned. Identification of the blastema with the young regenerate is an anachronism when, as in *T. viridescens,* it can be shown that blastema cell production begins well back in the old stump. In this species the forelimb blastema can be conceived as a mass of cells occupying not only the region distal to the amputation plane but also the space previously taken up by the now dissociated soft tissues of the subjacent stump. Only by the twenty-fifth day is the mitotic activity of the regenerating limb so clearly concentrated in the regenerate proper that it can be reasonably identified with the blastema. Unfortunately, this is also the date at which redifferentiation begins in the regenerate, and the number of blastema cells rapidly decreases.

During the early stages of blastema accumulation it is possible to identify a large number of mitoses with specific stump tissues. On the seventh day after amputation, approximately 68 per cent of all mitoses can be identified with residual stump tissues, while the remaining 32 per cent of the cell divisions are classed as blastema mitoses (Fig. 8). During the next 18 days the percentage of cell divisions identifiable only as blastema cell mitoses, since they show neither clearly identifiable morphologic characteristics nor close association with differentiated tissues, increases to a maximum of 89.9 per cent. All the identifiable mitoses are confined to the stump, but only a few perichondrial mitoses are associated with newly differentiating tissues. On the thirty-first day many new mitoses are identifiable in differentiating tissues, and by the thirty-seventh day only 30.8 per cent of the mitoses are still recognizable only as blastema cell divisions. By this latter date all the mitoses in differentiating cells are found in the regenerate. A comparison of the distribution of these mitoses to the various categories on the seventh day with that found on the thirty-first day (see Fig. 8), when plotted on a scatter diagram as in Figure 9, shows that a high degree of correlation exists between them. If correlation were perfect, all points would lie on the interrupted line, and the correlation coefficient, r, would have a value of 1.00. The value of r found for the observed scatter from perfect correlation is 0.965. The data indicate a very broad origin of the blastema cells from all the stump tissues and strongly suggest a possible tissue-specific origin—muscle contributing to muscle, connective tissue to connective tissue, and so on.

If this latter suggestion were true, a similarly close correlation should exist between the distribution of cells among the tissues of the unamputated limb (see Fig. 10, *A*) and the distribution of mitotic activity among the tissues of the regenerating limb (see Fig. 10, *D*). These are obviously not directly comparable, since there is no equivalent of the blastema cell in the unamputated limb. If, however, we distribute the blastema cell mitoses among the other categories in the proportions found among those tissues on the seventh day after regeneration (Fig. 8), we get the distribution shown in Figure 10, *B*. If this distribution of the total subepidermal mitoses is plotted against the distribution of subepidermal cells in unamputated limbs, as in the scatter diagram of Figure 11, a close correlation, in which the value of *r* is 0.960, is obtained. The only striking deviations from more perfect correlation are the low number of mitoses in the blood vessels (*BV*) and the high num-

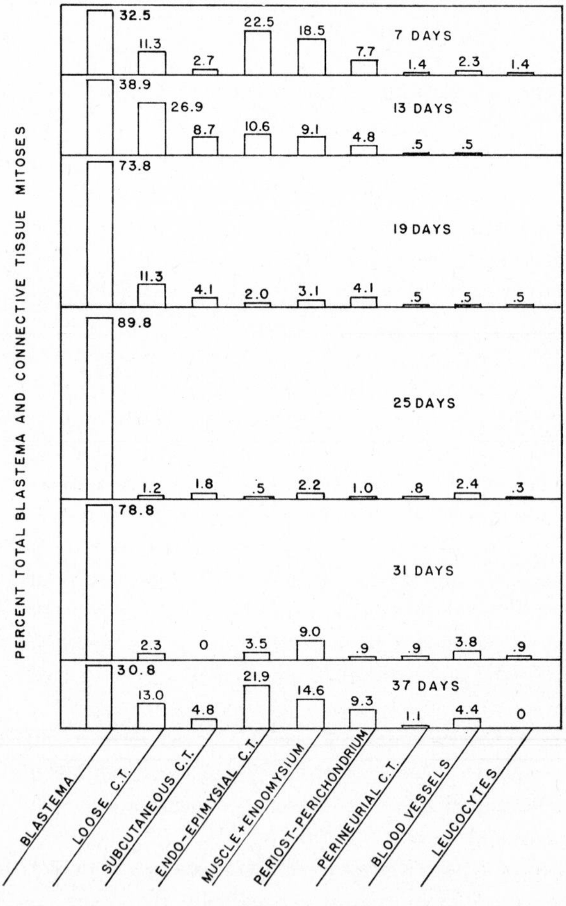

FIG. 8.—Percentages of the total blastema and connective tissue mitoses at 7, 13, 19, 25, 31, and 37 days after regeneration, attributable to various tissue components. (From Chalkley, 1954.)

ber of mitoses in the epimysium-endomysium (*EE*) categories. Since the small regenerate does not require the large, heavily walled arteries present in the normal limb, the first deviation is readily understandable. The high count in the epimysium-endomysium category is not so easily explained. Since most of the other counts are low, it may reflect a predilec-

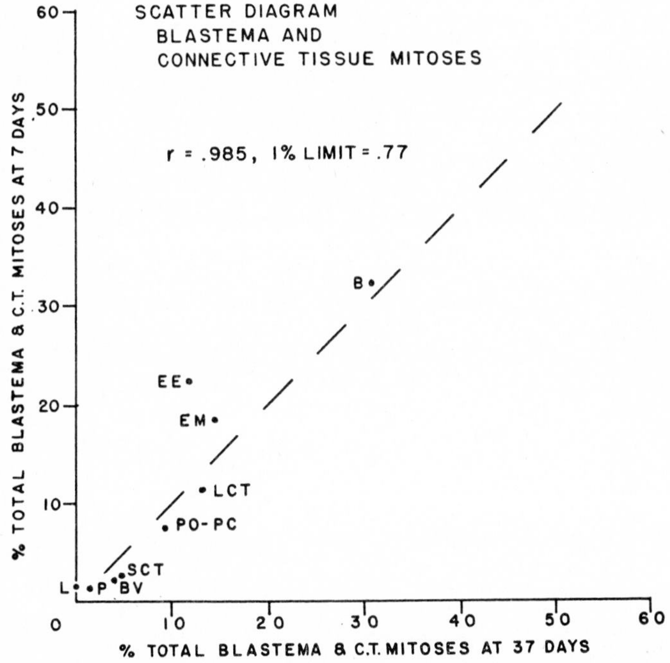

FIG. 9.—Scatter diagram, showing correlation between the distribution of the total blastema and connective tissue mitoses at 7 days as compared with their distribution at 37 days. The correlation coefficient, r, for this scatter is 0.985. The abbreviations are: *B*, blastema cells; *BV*, blood vessel walls; *EE*, epimysium and endomysium; *EM*, endomysium and muscle (assignment to *EE* or to muscle uncertain); *L*, leukocytes; *LCT*, loose connective tissue; *P*, perineurium; *PO-PC*, periosteum-perichondrium; *SCT*, subcutaneous connective tissue.

tion on the part of the investigator to place doubtful counts in this category.

We have now established correlation between mitotic activity in the stump tissues and in the redifferentiating regenerate tissues and between the distribution of cells in the normal limb and the mitotic activity in the regenerating limb. It now remains to establish the degree of correlation between mitotic activity in the regenerating limb (see Fig. 10, *B*) and the numbers of new cells produced (see Fig. 10, *C*). Only the first five

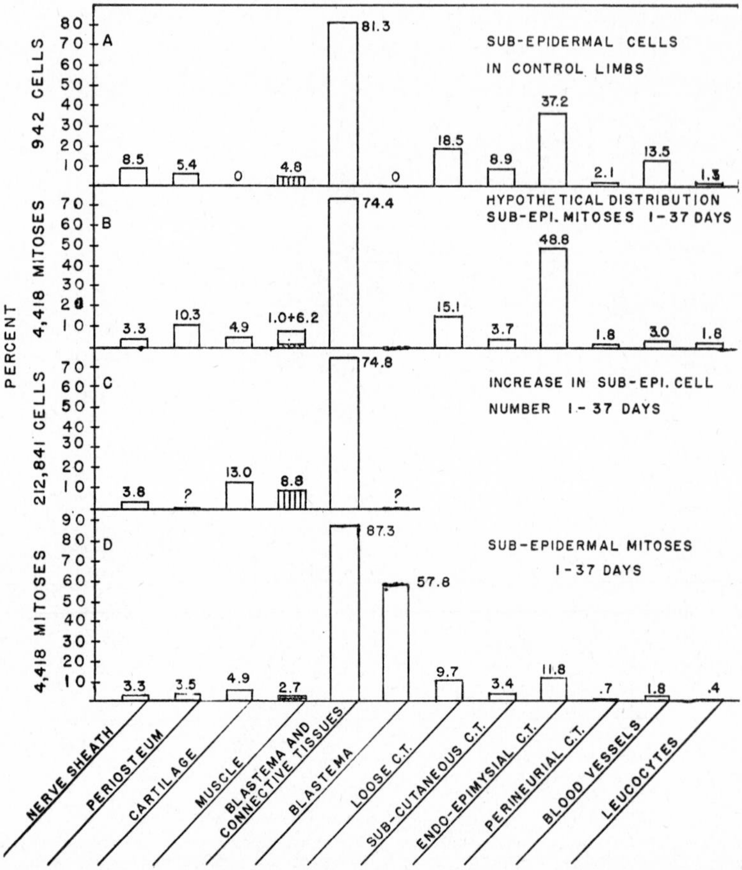

FIG. 10.—*A*, Distribution of subepidermal cells in the control limbs. *B*, Hypothetical distribution of subepidermal mitoses through the thirty-seventh day. These data were obtained by distributing the blastema mitoses among the possible connective tissue contributors on the basis of the distribution shown in Fig. 8 on the seventh day (see detailed explanation in text). *C*, Increase in cell number in the regenerating limbs through the thirty-seventh day. Periosteal cells are inseparable from cartilage. *D*, Distribution of subepidermal mitoses through the thirty-seventh day if blastema mitoses are counted as a distinct type (possible reserve cells?).

In all graphs the column "blastema and connective tissues" is the sum of all columns graphed to its right. Hatched portions of the muscle columns represent counts on intact muscle; clear portions represent counts in dissociated or redifferentiating muscle. (From Chalkley, 1954.)

categories—nerve sheath cells, periosteal cells, cartilage cells, muscle cells, and the combined blastema and connective tissue cells—can be compared in the scatter diagram in Figure 12. Routine identification of mitoses is possible because of the relatively small number of cells involved. Similar precision in identification of the various types of con-

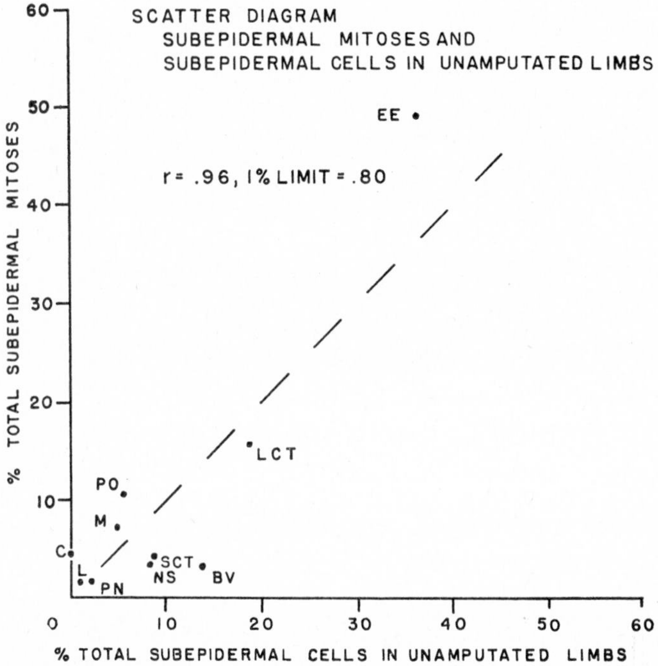

FIG. 11.—Scatter diagram, showing correlation between the distribution of the total subepidermal mitoses and the distribution of the subepidermal cells in the unamputated limb. The dashed line indicates the line of perfect correlation. The correlation coefficient, r, for this scatter is 0.96. The abbreviations are: *BV*, blood vessel walls; *C*, cartilage; *EE*, epimysium and endomysium (includes 75 per cent of *EM*, endomysium and muscle, mitoses); *L*, leukocytes; *LCT*, loose connective tissue; *M*, muscle (includes 25 per cent of *EM*, endomysium and muscle, mitoses); *NS*, nerve sheath; *PN*, perineurium; *PO*, periosteum; *SCT*, subcutaneous connective tissue.

nective tissue cells is impracticable, if not impossible. The correlation obtained with the raw data gives a high r value of 0.973, but, because of the small number of points, this is only slightly higher than the 1 per cent confidence limit of 0.96. The reason for this is readily evident. Periosteal divisions account for 10.3 per cent of the total mitoses, but there are no periosteal cells in the regenerate and no detectable new periosteal cells in the old stump. On the other hand, cartilage accounts for

13.0 per cent of the new cells but only 4.9 per cent of the mitoses. If we recognize the probability that periosteal and perichondrial cells represent different functional states of the same cell and that periosteal mitoses contribute to the formation of perichondrial, and thus cartilage, cells, then the number of cartilage-producing mitoses ($C + PO$ in Fig. 12) amounts to 15.2 per cent of the total number of cell divisions. This compares favorably with the 13.0 per cent of the new cells which are cartilage.

A similar adjustment can be made with respect to the formation of new muscle nuclei. These account for 8.8 per cent of the added cells and

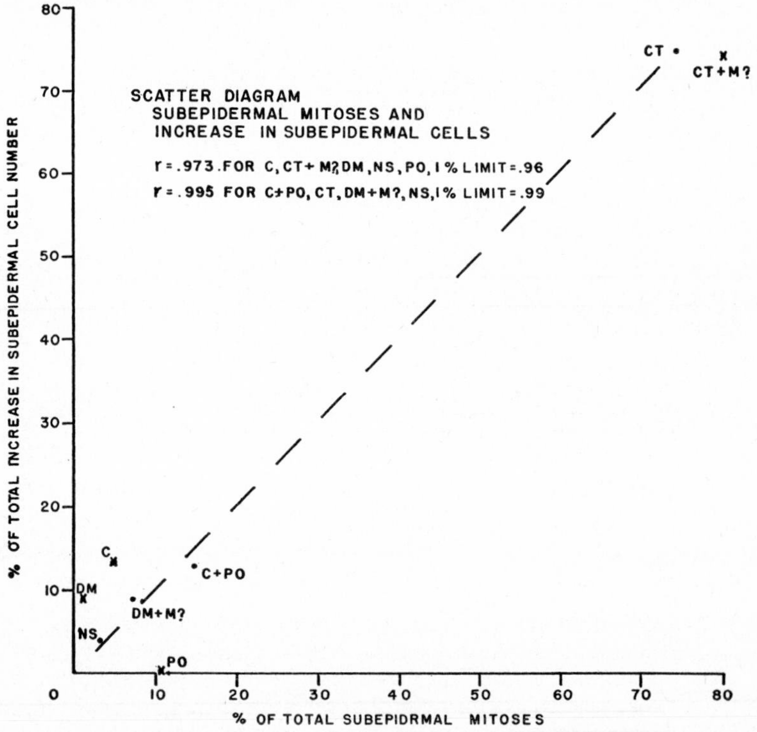

FIG. 12.—Scatter diagram, showing correlation between the distribution of the increase in subepidermal cell numbers in various categories and the distribution of mitoses in various similar or identical categories during the same period. The dashes indicate the line of perfect correlation. The correlation coefficient, *r*, for this scatter is 0.973 or 0.995, depending upon the selection of points (see text for details). The abbreviations are: *C*, cartilage; *PO*, periosteum; *C + PO*, cartilage plus periosteum; *CT*, connective tissue; *CT + M?*, connective tissue plus some probable muscle mitoses; *DM*, differentiated muscle tissue; *DM + M?*, cells and mitoses in differentiated muscle plus probable muscle mitoses; *NS*, nerve sheath cells and mitoses.

nuclei but for only 1.0 per cent of the contributory mitoses. However, certain of the mitoses occurring in the empty endomysial sheaths of the old stump cannot be clearly identified with either connective tissue or muscle (*CT* + *M?* in Fig. 12). Assuming that approximately 25 per cent of these mitoses are muscle, since 25 per cent of the nuclei in the normal muscle-enodomysium complex are in that category, they account for 6.2 per cent of the total mitoses. Adding the questionable muscle mitoses to mitoses in differentiated muscle tissue (*DM* + *M?* in Fig. 12), a close fit to perfect correlation is obtained. The fit of connective tissue mitoses and increase in connective tissue cell number is also improved. The value of *r* obtained with these modified data is appreciably higher, 0.995, though the elimination of a point by the combination of cartilage and periosteal cells and mitoses increases the value of the 1 per cent confidence limit to 0.99.

Correlation exists, then, between the distribution of available cells in the stump, the mitotic activity in the stump, the continued mitotic activity in the redifferentiating cells of the regenerate, the increase in cell number, and, since it is identical with availability, the ultimate demand for cells in the restored limbs. The correlation coefficients obtained range between 0.96 and 0.995 and are in excess of the 1 per cent confidence limits for each correlation.

Allowing for the necessary recapitulation of embryonic processes in the formation of bone, there is nothing in these data that would preclude their interpretation as a description of tissue-specific regeneration.

Such a conclusion is incompatible with pertinent experimental observations, particularly the X-radiation experiments of Thornton (1942), Luther (1948), Trampusch (1951), Rose, Quastler, and Rose (1953), and Ichikawa and Okada (1954). In all these experiments limbs have been exposed to X-ray doses sufficient to inhibit regeneration, and then various tissues have been replaced or supplemented with normal unirradiated tissues. The "radiation chimeras" thus produced formed regenerates with fair frequency and normality. Dr. Trampusch describes certain of these results elsewhere in this volume. There is no point in repeating them here. It is interesting to note that chimeras frequently develop normally, though the subcutaneous connective tissue is supposedly the only mitotically competent tissue present. Normally, it provides only 3.7 per cent of the mitoses. Where the mitotically competent tissue has been muscle, accompanied inevitably by the epimysium and endomysium, which normally provide 56 per cent of the mitoses, regenerates are infrequent and differentiate poorly.

It would be interesting to know the distribution of mitotic activity in these chimeras. Are the tissues of an irradiated limb equally inhibited? Does the addition of mitotically competent tissue to an irradiated limb in any way affect the mitotic activity of the irradiated tissues? Brunst and Chérémetiéva (1935) have found partial regeneration in 75 per cent of *Triturus* treated with 15,000 r. Fimian (1951) found near-normal mitotic activity in two out of fifteen limbs exposed to doses of 5,000 r. Litschko (1934) noted accelerated regeneration following removal of the dense wound epidermis formed by regenerates exposed to 300 r. Ichikawa and Okada (1954) added unirradiated hind-limb tissues to forelimbs which had been exposed to 1,000 r. Of the normal limbs regenerated, 62 per cent were forelimb in type. They suggest that irradiated tissues are somehow stimulated to recover their regenerative and proliferative capacities by the presence of normal tissue.

Lacking quantitative histologic studies on these radiation chimeras, we are forced to admit that a blastema can be formed in the absence of the usual contributing tissues. This is not a difficult admission to make where such tissues as the endomysium, endoneurium, and subcutaneous connective tissues are concerned, since there is little difference in the functions of their component cells. Cartilage and muscle present different problems. In the absence of unirradiated muscle or of unirradiated cartilage, perichondrium, or periosteum, what is the source of these tissues? It would seem necessary to propose the presence in the limb of indifferent reserve cells or of physiologically dedifferentiated cells. Brunst and Chérémtiéva (1936) suggested that the variability in the response of regenerating limbs to regeneration could be explained on the assumption that the limb contained a relatively small number of reserve cells. The widespread nature of the mitotic pool that produces the blastema would seem to rule out this particular hypothesis. Weiss (1923, 1939) has also proposed a reserve-cell origin of the blastema. He has pointed out that morphological dedifferentiation may occur with ease under tissue culture conditions, while the occurrence of physiologic dedifferentiation is extremely infrequent. In the absence of a mechanism for physiologic dedifferentiation or for the orderly migrations or reassociations required by tissue-specific regeneration, Weiss prefers to conceive of blastema formations as the result of the proliferation of reserve cells. To what extent is this a necessary device? Where are the reserve cells? Again we do not need to provide a reserve-cell mechanism for the connective tissues. They are ubiquitous and presumably easily mobilized into whatever categories are needed. The close association of connective tissues and the perichondrium and periosteum might form a basis for an argument that a residual ability to form cartilage and bone was retained by a large number of connective tissue elements. On the other hand, the distinctive behavior and appearance of the periosteal and perichondrial cells in the blastema suggest that they are truly distinct from the connective tissues. A reserve cell is therefore required which can differentiate into cartilage and muscle cells and possibly into connective tissue cells. No distinctive reserve cell appears to be present, and it seems surprising, if such cells are present, "disguised" as normal tissue cells, that they are so uniformly distributed throughout all the normal tissues of the limb and are not limited to a single mitotically competent cell type, such as the fibroblast, as inferred by Manner (1953). One could, of course, argue that some of the mitoses observed in the limb are those of differentiated cells dividing cell-specifically and that only a small fraction of the divisions are those of reserve cells. At the moment this possibility would have to be admitted, though the distinct periosteal divisions would argue against it.

The physiologic conservatism of cultivated tissues constitutes an argument against the reserve-cell hypothesis, as well as against the hypothesis of dedifferentiation. The persistent retention of physiologic characteristics by gonadotrophin-secreting chorionic cells (Waltz *et al.*, 1954), of glycogen retention by cultivated liver cells (Westfall *et al.*, 1953), and the reversion to their characteristic epithelial patterns of fibroblast-like skin cells following their return to an in vivo environment (Bassett *et al.*, 1955) suggest that functional dedifferentiation of adult tissues may be a myth. But tissue culture has also failed to disclose any reserve-cell potentials in the variety of cells included in the culture inoculum, even though they have been exposed to a variety of culture environments. Cultivation in vitro of blastema cells produces cultures that are indistinguishable from connective tissue cultures obtained from non-regenerating parts of the organism (Lecamp, 1947, 1949).

We are faced with a dilemma. Radiation chimeras and extirpation experiments clearly suggest the existence of some *doppelte Sicherung* mechanism in the regenerating limb. Other experiments fail to identify either a dedifferentiating mechanism or a reserve-cell system that could explain the ability of the limb to regenerate normally when certain characteristic tissues are absent from the amputation plane. Clearly, we need to know more about the behavior of irradiated cells and tissues. Does irradiation block mitosis completely and permanently? What tissues in a radiation chimera are dividing? Following extirpation of limb parts, are there any changes in the rates of division of the cells near the amputation plane? Over what distances can mitotically competent cells migrate to reach the blastema?

Quantitative histologic techniques can help to answer some of these questions, albeit in a slow and cumbersome fashion. The use of tagged cell-specific or even tissue-specific antibodies as tracers for morphologically dedifferentiated cells would be of considerable help. The development of "tissue pure" radiation chimeras which avoid the complications of previous experiments which always involved the transfer of some mitotically competent connective tissue would present a surgical challenge of no small magnitude. Only with a considerable advance in our present knowledge of the histology, histochemistry, and physiology of the blastema, can we hope to be in a position to place any reliance on any of the currently available hypotheses as to the nature of the regeneration process.

DISCUSSION

Discussion leader: PAUL WEISS, *Rockefeller Institute for Medical Research*

In opening the discussion, DR. WEISS remarked on the great advances that have taken place in our understanding of regeneration in the last few decades, but he emphasized the great amount of work still to be done, particularly in arriving at an understanding of the processes of differentiation within the regenerate. The sources of the cells of regeneration are, he believes, pretty well on the way to being determined, as Dr. Chalkley's paper so well indicates. In support of the diverse origins of blastema cells, he referred to his histologic demonstration in 1927 of at least the peri- and intramuscular, the perineural, the periosteal, and the perichondrial sheaths as active sources.

Now, however, attention should be directed to the activities of these cells. How do they migrate to the limb tip, for example? Why do they move? There are, in regenerating limbs, mass migrations of cells which move between other cells, but how? Why do they accumulate in a blastema? Why do not the regeneration cells move back into the stump instead of to the limb tip? We have always called on the concept of "polarity" to account for this, but it is now time to replace this word "polarity" with concrete knowledge and find out why cells move as they do.

In the blastema we have an accumulation of cells which have become scrambled; they are derived from various sources, but apparently they sort themselves out according to their properties. Thus, for example, the muscle cells must do this, for how do they get to where muscle belongs? One must remember that muscle is specific as to kind. How do specific kinds of muscles get to the right places? The flexors are always on the flexor side and the extensors on the extensor side. Similarly, cartilage cells seem to "know" what kind of architecture to build up. "This problem hasn't even been touched, so let's point it up as something to investigate."

DR. WEISS pointed out that, fortunately, help in this problem is coming from studies other than those concerned with regeneration—from tissue culture studies in which we learn what separated cells can do when reunited in a new assembly. Thus in experiments of Weiss and Andres, mechanically dissociated whole 1 to 2 day chick blastoderm cells were injected into the blood stream of older host embryos. Some of the cells were caught in loops of the yolk sac and formed highly organized teratomata with cartilage, spinal ganglia, bone, and other tissues. Thus these separated cells, when recombined, will form highly organized structures. Individually, they "know" how, once combined, to reassociate into specific tissues. Moscona dissociated limb-bud cartilage cells by the use of trypsin, and these cells formed limb cartilage even when transplanted out into a plasma clot. Dr. Weiss described experiments (Weiss and James) involving the dissociation by trypsin of skin from 8-day chick embryos. When these scrambled cells were reassembled and placed on a plasma clot, they became organized into feather germs as well as skin. Furthermore, Weiss and Moscona dissociated the cells of the cartilage of the sclera of the chick's eye, which grows as a plate, and brought them together again and placed them on a plasma clot. Here they formed a scleral plate of cartilage. Again, it is as though the separated cells "know" what sort of architecture to form when they come together again. As Dr. Weiss points out, we have here a situation that seems to parallel that of regeneration, and when we learn more about the conditions under which organized structures can re-form from scrambled cells, then we shall know how cells of a regeneration blastema, derived from various sources and naturally scrambled, can reassort into the new tissue of the regenerate.

In the general discussion which followed these remarks of Dr. Weiss, Dr. Lehmann presented data which indicated that the activities of the enzyme kathepsin, in the regenerating tail of *Xenopus* larvae, paralleled the migratory activities of the cells of regeneration as described by Dr. Chalkley. Thus in the normally regenerating tail there is a steep rise in the activity of kathepsin to a maximum on the seventh day after amputation, that is, just before growth starts. Chemically inhibited amputated tails, however, exhibited a uniformly high kathepsin activity even after the seventh day. Dr. Lehmann expressed the belief that further study of the protein-splitting systems will be an invaluable aid to our understanding of the processes of regeneration.

Dr. Brunst expressed agreement with Dr. Chalkley on the lack of any evidence that the epidermis contributes cells to the regenerate. He reported that local X-radiation of the blastema inhibits regeneration and that even when adjacent non-irradiated skin migrates to cover the X-radiated blastema, no recuperation of regeneration occurs.

Dr. Butler congratulated Dr. Chalkley on his presentation of quantitative data which help clear up problems that have involved so many years of work by many investigators using qualitative methods. Furthermore, he indicated that he was particularly pleased that Dr. Chalkley found no sharp line of demarcation between the stump tissues and the blastema, and he felt that one might even dispense with the term "blastema," since we are dealing essentially with activities of tissues not only at the amputation surface but proximal to it as well, as Dr. Chalkley's quantitative data show. The blastema is part of a whole picture and not a separate entity at all. Concerning the remarks of Dr. Weiss, Dr. Butler commented that, in experiments of his own, of Dr. Deck, and of Dr. Dent on reversed limbs in urodeles, great cellular disorganization resulted perforce from the reversal of the limb axis but nevertheless these cells were capable of organizing themselves into a new structure which formed at the wrong end of the limb. There would seem to be, he thought, a point of meeting here between the kind of disorganized cell aggregate that Dr. Weiss is dealing with in his chick embryos and these reversed limbs, since there is built up here an aggregation of cells which somehow "know" what to form—limb structures. Much could be learned from a further examination of situations in which cells, from either the limb or the tail, might be studied under conditions in which they were to a great extent removed from the original organization.

Dr. Schotté agreed with the conclusions of Dr. Chalkley that the blastema is not sharply demarcated from the stump tissues. Experiments in his laboratory involving exarticulation of the humerus indicate that the blastema cells arise along the whole length of the canal of the old humerus.

Dr. Singer asked Dr. Chalkley if he had observed any preferential pathway of outflow of cells to the blastema. Dr. Chalkley replied that, unfortunately, his sections were cut transversely and so provided a poor method for such an analysis. Dr. Weiss, however, stated that there are cell streams along the nerves, but, since the nerves lie in liquid spaces between the muscles, this may merely represent a path of least resistance.

· IV ·

The Influence of Nerves on Regeneration[1]

MARCUS SINGER

Department of Zoölogy, Cornell University, Ithaca, New York

In 1823, Tweedy John Todd, English medical doctor, philosopher, and experimentalist, wrote, among other observations, as follows concerning his experiments on regeneration of the limb of the aquatic salamander:

> If the sciatic nerve be intersected at the time of amputation, that part of the stump below the section of the nerve mortifies. . . . If the division of the nerve be made after the healing of the stump, reproduction is either retarded or entirely prevented. And if the nerve be divided after reproduction has commenced, or considerably advanced, the new growth either remains stationary, or it wastes, becomes shrivelled and shapeless, or entirely disappears. This derangement cannot, in my opinion, be fairly attributed to the vascular derangement induced in the limb by the wound of the division, but must arise from something peculiar in the nerve.

One hundred years passed before his conclusions were accepted; but it is a fact today, with little dispute, that without the nerve the limb of the salamander does not regenerate.[2] Indeed, the dependence upon the nerve may be stated as a general rule not only for the urodele amphibian but for other vertebrates as well. Such diverse forms as the fish and lizard (Kamrin and Singer, 1955*a, b*), the salamander (reviewed by Rose, 1948; Singer, 1952), and the larval anuran (Schotté and Harland, 1943) require the nerve to regenerate extremities. It may also be possible to extend this rule to invertebrates (Korschelt, 1927; Needham, 1952). The nervous system is less discrete in these forms and is therefore more difficult to operate on; however, available experimental information bespeaks a dependence of organ regeneration upon the nervous system in these forms as well. Thus the influence of the nervous system upon the

1 Supported in part by grants from the American Cancer Society and from the National Institutes of Health.

2 A notable exception is to be found in the work of Yntema (1949), who observed that larval limbs that develop in the absence of nerve do not require nerves for regeneration and that if such limbs are later supplied with nerve, they regenerate supernumerary structures (report to this congress).

reproduction of bodily parts is not unique within the vertebrate group but, along with other more generally recognized trophic[3] influences on the maintenance and well-being of adult tissues, has a history which begins probably at the same time that the neuron first appeared as a separate and distinct unit. If not in the physiologic sense, then at least in the evolutionary one, the trophic activity of nerve fibers is as fundamental as the one of conduction, with which, indeed, it may share a common biochemical mechanism (see below).

The control which the nerve exerts upon growth is all the more striking when one considers how difficult it is to suppress regeneration by other means, a fact which Todd appreciated when he also remarked:

> It is a most difficult task, and I may almost say, a fruitless one, to endeavor to induce a derangement in the process of reproduction. It is, however, a pleasing one to observe the new means by which nature is ever prepared to adapt herself to every new circumstance and exigency.

The march of regenerative events is an inexorable one, even under such unfavorable circumstances as infusions of acid, alkali, and solutions of various salt contents (Singer, Flinker, and Sidman, 1955). Yet, when the nerve is withdrawn, the effect is immediate and dramatic: regeneration does not occur, and, if the nerve is transected during the early formative stages of regeneration, the new growth "wastes, becomes shriveled and shapeless, or entirely disappears." Another remarkable fact about the nerve action is that the neuron—the source of the effect on growth—is one of the most adult of cells, being highly differentiated morphologically and highly specialized physiologically. Ordinarily, it is not considered to have much growth potential, since it is unable to divide and since destruction of the cell is not followed by replacement. Actually, however, the neuron, despite its specialization and advanced differentiation, is in reality an ever youthful cell because its protoplasmic processes, which make up the bulk of the cell, are restless and are continuously being extended, reworked, retracted, and re-formed. To this end, as well as for maintenance of the processes, a continuous flow of substances moves along the axis cylinder from the cell body to the periphery. This flow apparently reflects the tremendous need in protein and other metabolic substances required by continuous peripheral growth and adjustment. It may be that the effect which neurons have upon the growth of the regenerate represents a spilling-over, so to speak,

[3] The term "trophic" as employed in the literature has a variety of implied meanings (Parker, 1932). It is used here as a short and useful term to mean the morphologic and developmental dependence which tissues show upon the integrity of the nerve.

of the growth and maintenance activity of the nerve. In this way, therefore, the influence may be one and the same with the growth and trophic maintenance of the fiber itself.

RESPONSE OF AMPUTATION STUMP AND REGENERATE TO DENERVATION

The events that follow denervation vary according to the time after amputation when denervation is performed (see reviews, Rose, 1948; Singer, 1952). Before discussing these events, it would be well to describe, first, the sequence of normal regeneration, since the problem under discussion naturally follows from such a description. The description will be confined to limb regeneration in the urodele amphibian, which is favored in studies of the influence of the nerve on growth. Within about a day after amputation, the epidermis covers the wound, and wound reactions such as tissue breakdown, intense phagocytosis, and formation of scar tissue settle in. This phase lasts about 5 days in the adult and less in the larva. Thereafter, there occurs with increasing intensity a phase of dissolution of the fibrocellular wound tissue and adjacent tissues of the stump, such as muscle, tendon, and other connective tissue. This stage is frequently referred to as the phase of "dedifferentiation," since the appearance of cells of regeneration attends the tissue destruction. In the larva the cartilaginous skeleton is involved but less so the bony one of the adult. The epidermis thickens and eventually may have 12 or more layers of cells in contrast to the normal adult number of 3 or 4 (see Pl. I, Fig. 2). Associated with the tissue breakdown and other changes characterizing this period, there is the appearance of "cells of regeneration," also called "blastemal cells" or "mesenchymatous cells" (Pl. I, Fig. 2). They are scattered among the old tissues of the wound area and collect in increasing numbers under the epidermis to form the blastema.[4] The cells look like mesenchymal cells of the embryo, being morphologically undifferentiated and having processes which extend in various directions to form a loose syncytium. The origin of these cells is not known. They seem to arise from among the adult tissues by a process of dedifferentiation,[5] according to some workers, or by modulation of a

[4] The term "blastema" is used rather loosely in the literature on regeneration to mean the mesenchymatous accumulation with its epidermal covering or the subepidermal portion alone. I shall use the term in the latter sense in this work.

[5] The term "dedifferentiation" is also employed loosely in the literature but is used here to mean the return of cells and tissues to a morphologically simple state resembling the cells or tissues of the embryo, without implying in the definition that these cells and tissues have at the same time recaptured the developmental potentialities of embryonic ones.

PLATE I

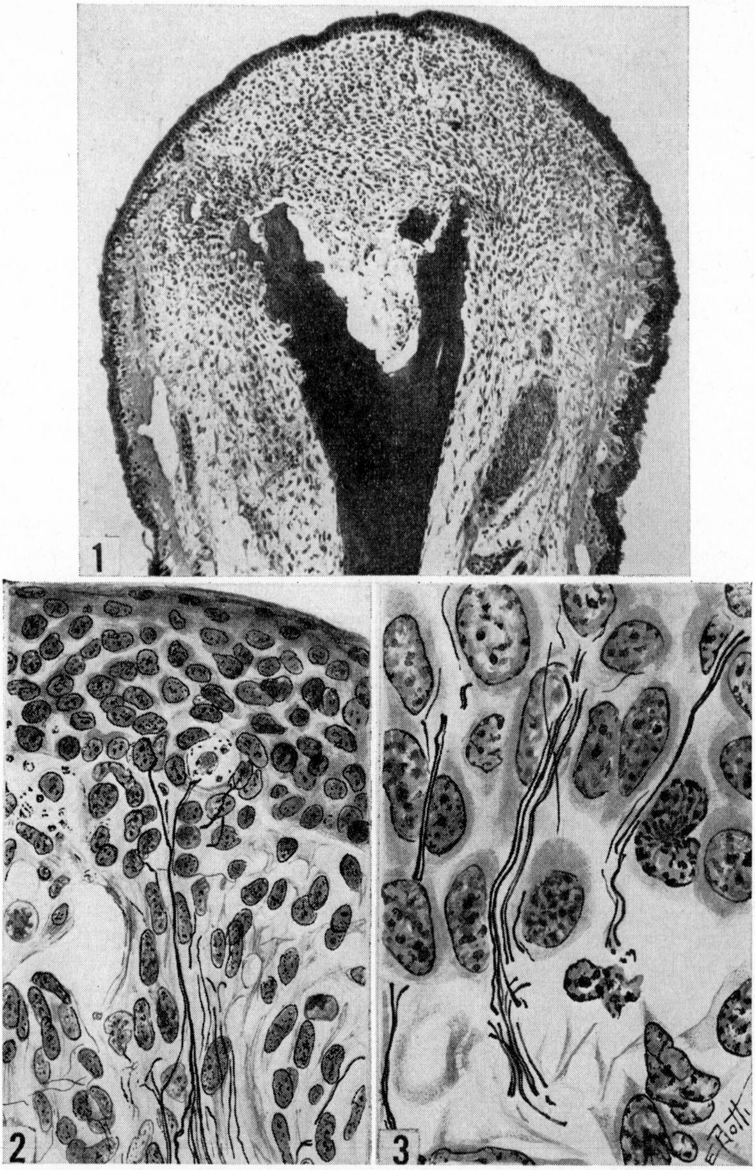

FIG. **1.**—Early regenerate bud of the upper arm in longitudinal section, showing the blastema with its many mesenchymatous cells. Note the thickened distal epithelium, and compare it with the proximal one; note the central bony shaft and the nerve to the right. Taken from Fig. 3 of Singer, Weinberg, and Sidman (1955). ×48.

FIG. 2.—Selected view of a longitudinal section of an early regenerate stained with silver, showing a nerve fascicle invading the distal epithelium. Note the many cells of the blastema oriented along the bundle, the great thickness of the epidermis, and the general similarity in appearance of the mesenchymatous cells. Taken from Fig. 8, Singer (1949). Approximately ×280.

FIG. 3.—Longitudinal silvered section of early regenerate bud at border region between epidermis and blastema, showing nerve fibers invading the epidermis. Note the apparent looseness of the epidermal cells, the intercellular position of the nerve fibers, the lack of a basal membrane beneath the epidermis, and the scattered mesenchymatous cells below. Approximately ×1,300.

reserve type of cell scattered among the tissues, according to others. Whatever their origin, these cells gradually accumulate under the wound epidermis in the later days of this phase to form the blastema; the enlarging structure having the appearance of a bud is often called an "early regenerate bud" (Pl. I, Fig. 1). This phase of regeneration is therefore characterized by two major events: the appearance of cells of regeneration accompanied by widespread histolysis and, second, the aggregation of these cells under the wound epithelium to form the blastema.

There then follows a stage of very rapid growth of the bud characterized by numerous mitoses. At the same time there is a decrease and then a cessation in the breakdown of stump tissues. The rate of increase is great at first, and the regenerate becomes visibly elongated within a few days (see stages of Singer, 1952). Then follows the prolonged terminal phase of morphologic and histologic differentiation, which is accompanied by progressive decline in the rate of growth.

The division of regeneration into precise phases is, of course, arbitrary and is done here only for convenience in subsequent descriptions of the nerve influence on growth. Actually, it is more correct to speak of a predominance of events characterizing a stage rather than an exclusiveness, since there is considerable overlap of successive stages.

In all the phases of regeneration except the first day or two after amputation, the nerve is present in the form of regenerating twigs and trunks among the wound and regenerate tissues (Singer, 1949*b*). The invasion is a very rich one, and the nerve pervades the growth in all its parts (Pl. I, Figs. 2 and 3). It grows with abandon among the regenerating tissues, particularly in the blastema, where conditions appear most conducive to fiber growth. Of special interest is the growth of fibers in number into the epidermis (Singer, 1949*a*, *b*), to the significance of which I shall refer later. In non-regenerating skin, only an occasional fiber is present in the epidermis, and it is generally confined to the basal epidermal layer. But in the epidermis of the early regenerate there are large numbers of nerve fibers (Pl. I, Figs. 2 and 3) which grow in all directions and are even exposed at the free surface. The fibers may be individual or in fascicles, they are naked, and they appear to be intercellular in position. The number of fibers per unit area of epidermis declines in later stages of regeneration and approaches the distribution of non-regenerating skin. The rich innervation of the epithelium of the urodele regenerate is supported in similar findings by Taban (1949, 1955). They have been reported in larval urodele and anuran regenerates by Thornton (1954, 1956), in the regenerating barbel of the catfish

(Kamrin and Singer, 1955), and in the induced regenerate of the limb of the postmetamorphic frog (Singer, unpublished).

If the stump of the adult animal is denervated at the time of amputation, regeneration does not occur, provided that a relatively nerveless condition is maintained. However, there is wound healing and eventual regeneration of a relatively normal skin over the amputation surface. Tissue debris is removed by phagocytes of various sorts, but there is no prolonged histolysis of tissues subjacent to the wound, and the epidermis does not thicken as it would in a regenerating stump. Associated with the slight breakdown of adult tissues is the paucity or absence of cells of regeneration, and, therefore, a dependent relation may be drawn between the appearance of cells of regeneration and the presence of nerve. There is evidence of regeneration of tissues other than skin when the nerve is absent. This regeneration, however, is limited and confined to the immediate vicinity of the wound. There is formation of fibrocellular connective tissue, some muscle and tendon regrowth, and frequently the development of a cap and sleeve of cartilage around the end of the humerus. Although further information is needed on the relation between tissue regeneration and the nerve, denervation thus does not entirely suppress the regeneration of tissues, and, indeed, the skin seems hardly affected at all. What is especially affected is regeneration of the organ, the most characteristic event of which is the formation of the blastema (Pl. I, Fig. 1). It is important to stress that it is organ formation particularly and tissue regeneration only secondarily that are influenced by the nerve. Morgan was concerned with this thought in his attempt to explain the lack of extremity regeneration in higher forms. For example, he states in his studies of the importance of the nerve cord in regeneration of the worm (1902) the following opinion, which Holmes (1931) shares and further emphasizes:

> Each of the different kinds of tissue can no doubt regenerate its like without the presence of the nervous system, but that the new tissues should become organized into a new whole structure the presence of the nervous system is requisite.

And, in his lecture of 1906 (p. 229), he remarked concerning regeneration in man ". . . the failure of the new limb to develop does not appear to be due to the failure of the individual elements to regenerate."

The consequences of denervation at the time of amputation are more far-reaching in the larval than in the adult urodele. At first, wound healing occurs, but then widespread histolysis of subepidermal tissues of the wound sets in, and mesenchymatous cells, presumably similar to those observed in normal regeneration, are freed (Schotté and Butler, 1941); however, these fail to accumulate in the amputation area but, instead, are destroyed. Moreover, the stump continues to "dedifferentiate" unchecked and to resorb in a gradual distal-proximal sweep until the entire stump is gone (Pl. II, Figs. 4–6). Should nerve fibers regrow into the stump, resorption is checked, and regeneration is initiated. Therefore, besides regeneration, the morphologic integrity of the stump requires the nerve (see also Thornton and Kraemer, 1951; Thornton, 1953), an arrangement also observed in the barbel of the catfish (Kamrin and Singer, 1955). Butler and Schotté emphasize that failure of these cells to accumulate under the wound epithelium to form a blastema is the major consequence of denervation and that accumulation, in turn, somehow checks further dedifferentiation and resorption (Schotté, Butler, and Hood, 1941). It may be that the nerve serves to brake the sweep of histolysis initiated by wounding (Thornton, 1953).

If the stump is denervated, not at the time of amputation but later, when the blastema is being formed, regeneration ceases, and, except for some tissue differentiation, there is no further growth in the adult. The same occurs if denervation is delayed until the blastema stage (early bud) at a time when rapid growth has been initiated; there is a notable drop in the mitotic rate after an initial outburst of divisions in response to loss of the nerve (Singer and Craven, 1948); the regenerate "shrivels and wastes." There is then formation of connective tissue, cartilage, and muscle at the expense of the denervated blastema. In the larva, regeneration also ceases if denervation is performed up to the time when the blastema is well formed, and, after some hesitation in the latter stage (see Pl. III, Fig. 7) but more promptly in the earlier, resorptive and destructive processes prevail (Schotté and Butler, 1944; Butler and Schotté, 1949). Therefore, the nerve is needed throughout the early postamputation days and until the time when the accumulation blastema has begun to grow rapidly. The latter stage of growth Butler and Schotté call the "phase of induction," "when the blastema is converted into a true regenerate with morphogenetic potencies."

If the denervation is performed slightly later, the blastema of the adult animal is fashioned into a small limb containing differentiated tissues. The growth is characterized by axial elongation but no increase in volume (Singer and Craven, 1948). The regenerate of the larva of a given size also grows and develops after interruption of the nerve (Schotté and Butler, 1944), although the extent of independence of the nerve influence has not been measured quantitatively. Therefore, one may conclude that, beyond a certain stage of development, the nerve is no longer required for regeneration; or perhaps it may be more accurate to state, instead, that, once the nerve has played upon the wound tissues for an adequate time and a blastema has been formed and has attained a

PLATE II

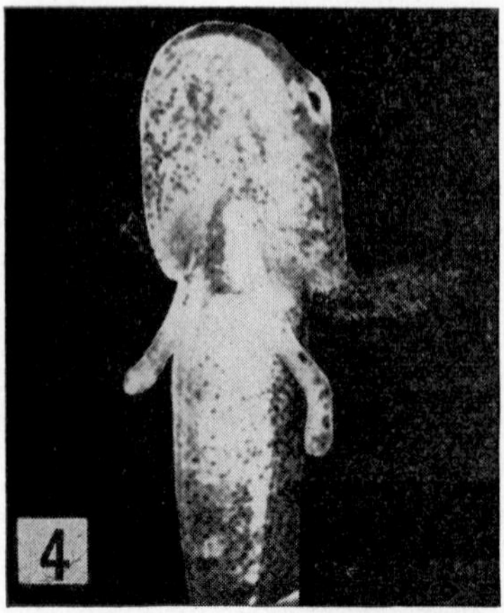

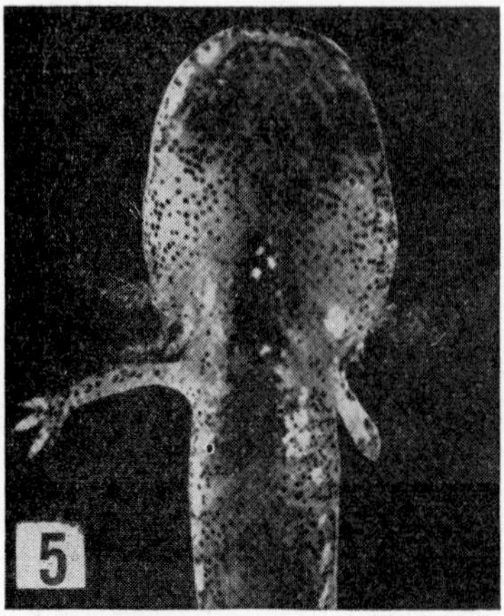

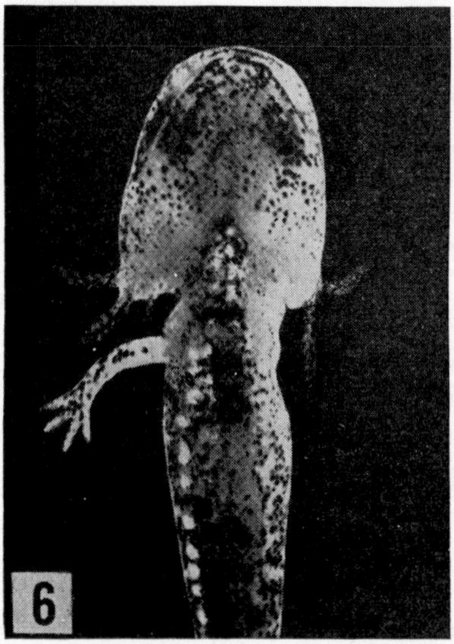

FIGS. 4–6.—To show the resorption of the larval limb stump after denervation and amputation. Taken from Figs. 17–19 of Schotté and Butler (1941). Both sides amputated through the metacarpals, and left side denervated at same time. Fig. *4*, 8 days after operation; Fig. *5*, 22 days; Fig. *6*, 36 days. Note sequence of distoproximal resorption of stump. *Amblystoma opacum.*

given volume, then the growth can proceed, with some limitations, in the absence of the nerve.

In summary, then, the nerve is needed for "the normal process of dedifferentiation" (in the words of Schotté and Butler, 1944), for the actual appearance of mesenchymatous cells, at least in the case of the adult animal, and for accumulation of these cells at the amputation surface. The nerve is also needed for cellular division, and it may exert a control over tissue breakdown.

MECHANISM OF NERVE ACTION

A central problem in the study of the influence of the nerve upon regeneration is the nature of the nerve contribution. There is no information today on how nerves express themselves upon the new growth. How-

PLATE III

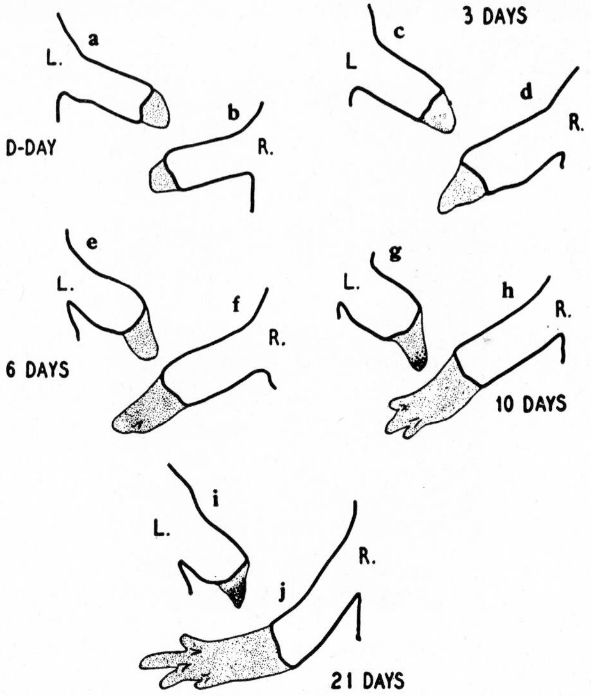

FIG. 7.—To show the consequences of denervation of a larval regenerate in the blastema stage, 7 days after amputation. The denervated regenerate (*left forelimb, L*) in contrast to the right (*R*) grew hesitatingly, then stopped and showed signs of regression in subsequent days (drawn 3, 6, 10, and 21 days after the day of denervation—D-day). Taken from Fig. 5 of Schotté and Butler (1944). *Amblystoma opacum.*

ever, given the recent history of analysis of the nerve influence, it is possible to pose this problem more precisely and speculate along lines which seem more reasonable than heretofore. There are a number of ways in which the nerve can conceivably contribute to growth, and salient among these are the ones discussed below.

1. The nerve may serve as a highway for the accumulation of cellular elements at the surface of amputation. Nerve fibers invade the amputation area even before mesenchymatous cells appear. They grow distally from the major trunks in large fascicles and from lesser branches and individual fibers. Schwann cells are known to migrate along these delicate threads. Perhaps other cells are also impelled to follow this route for some reason of selective affinity for the axis cylinder (see orientation of cells along neuraxis in Pl. I, Fig. 2). Thus regenerating nerve fibers may serve as preferential pathways for distal cellular migration—a movement which is required for accumulation of the blastema. Not only may cellular accumulation be an important function of the nerve, but the nerve may also play a leading role in the determination of the polarity of the regenerate (see Needham, 1952, pp. 74, 88). Of all the regenerating tissues, the neuraxis is the most polarized in its growth and in its morphology. In the normal stump the pressure of nerve growth is ever distal, and the growth of other tissues may be influenced by this force. On the basis of the ever distal growth of new fibers, it may be possible to explain why even reversed stumps develop only distal elements from the exposed amputation surface (Dent, 1954; Butler, 1955; Deck, 1955).

Even if the nerve fiber itself is not the railway for the accumulation of mesenchymatous cells, it may be that nerve fibers, because of the polarization of their growth, cause a general orientation of the ground substance of the stump and thus favor a predominantly distal direction of cellular migration. Thus the nerve trunks of many sizes and the myriad individual fibers with which the stump abounds may be thought of as fountains of cellular outpourings which follow the direction imposed by the nerve. Some unpublished work of one of my students (Eva Ray) lends some support to this notion. If the mesenchymatous cells of a localized area of the early regenerate are stained vitally with Nile blue sulfate according to the method of infusion (Singer, Weinberg, and Sidman, 1955), then gross distal movements of the marked region may be observed as the regenerate develops. However, the extent of distal movement varies according to the region of the regenerate stained. The dorsal and anterior quadrants of the early regenerate show little distal movement with subsequent growth; but there is extensive distal movement of the stained ventral and posterior quadrants. The major nerve trunks are located in the latter quadrants, and thus the region of greatest growth pressure of the regenerate appears to conform with the position of the nerve. In a previous work in which regeneration of the forelimb of the frog was induced by deviating the sciatic nerve to the forelimb and thus augmenting the nerve supply, I noted that the new growth tended to stem from the vicinity of greatest concentration of nerve trunks and thence spread to encompass the rest of the amputation area. Therefore, it may well be that the greatest growth impetus occurs in the immediate vicinity of highest nerve concentration. This may be due to the direct effect of nerve pathways upon cellular movements. Another possibility, which is considered in part later, is that the apparent movement is due to distal displacement of cells attending rapid cellular divisions localized in the vicinity of highest nerve concentration.

2. The nerve may contribute cellular elements of its own to the formation of the blastema. This idea has already been expressed in one form or another in the literature. Guyénot and Schotté (1926) at one time favored the possibility that cells of the new sheath moving out of the nerve into the wound area gave rise to the blastema, a possibility which seemed most interesting, since it was found then that heterotopic growth could be evoked at the site of deviation of the nerve to a new locus (Locatelli, 1924, 1929; Guyénot and Schotté, 1926; some recent researches on nerve deviations are those of Bovet, 1930; Kiortsis, 1953; Taban, 1955). The notion was not pursued further by Guyénot and his students, and, instead, the view that the general connective tissues are the source of mesenchymatous elements was favored (Guyénot, 1927). Thornton (1938), in his histologic studies of the regenerate of the larval urodele, implicated "sheath cells" of the nerve (presumably, the connective tissue sheath) as one of the sources of the blastema. Finally, Chalkley (1954) reported in his quantitative studies that the nerve in the immediate vicinity of the amputation contributed about 20 per cent of its cells to the blastema. However, he noted that these cells made up only a few per cent of the total cellular outflow from the stump into the regenerate.

The cells arising from the nerve and destined for the blastema may be of two major sorts. First, there are connective tissue elements with which the nerve abounds and which are contained in the various sheaths that invest the nerve and its fibers. Then there are the cells of the sheath of Schwann (neurilemma), which, once freed of their sheath, presumably move out along the regenerating axis cylinder into the blastema and multiply as they cling to the parent fiber. One does observe, in sections stained for axis cylinders, cells oriented along the fibers (see, e.g., Pl. I, Fig. 2). These may be Schwann cells, but there is no certainty about the identification, and, indeed, cells of the blastema, whatever their origin, appear very similar (Pl. I, Fig. 2). How much of the blastema is made up of Schwann cells and whether these cells contribute in some way to the nerve effect on growth is not known. It is, of course, difficult to imagine that Schwann cells form any other tissue than that of their origin; yet, until there is information to the contrary, this possibility must be weighed. The histology of the major nerve trunks at the level of amputation support the notion of cellular outflow from the nerve itself, since the trunk thins out as the blastema is formed and there is an obvious stream of cells along the outgrowing axis cylinders, whatever the nature of these cells may be.

In connection with the possibility that cells of the nerve might help to form the regenerate, some experiments of Professor Trampusch reported at this symposium and similar unpublished ones of my former student, Kamrin, are of interest. If the major nerves of the forelimb of the adult urodele (Kamrin) or of the hind limb of the larva (Trampusch) are dissected free and protected from irradiation while the freshly amputated stump is exposed to X-rays and if the nerve is then replaced in its original position, the stump will regenerate; but stumps in which the nerves are not protected from irradiation do not grow. Non-irradiated tissue, other than nerve, can also evoke growth when substituted for its kind in the irradiated stump (for example, muscle: Thornton, 1942; skin: Luther, 1948; regenerating skin: Rose, 1955; Trampusch, 1951). By what means the unaffected tissue causes or induces regeneration is not known. The unirradiated tissue may provide the cells for regeneration, or it may be that the regenerative capacity of irradiated tissue is recalled in some way by the implanted unirradiated tissue. If the former is the case, then cellular elements of the nerve can serve as the source of mesenchymatous cells. Perhaps under such circumstances the nerve, ordinarily a minor source of cells of regeneration (Chalkley, 1954), compensates for the loss of the other major contributing sources by multiplying its effectiveness.

Even if the nerve ordinarily does, or under special experimental circumstances can, serve as an important source of cells of regeneration, it must be stressed that such a contribution cannot occur in the absence of axis cylinders. In the absence of axis cylinders, cellular elements of the nerve remain in the stump and amputation area. Therefore, the contingency of intact axis cylinders must always serve as a background for any speculation on the nature of the nerve action in regeneration. Consequently, it is of first importance that the role of the neuraxis be carefully evaluated.

3. The most widely held or implied view of the mechanism of the nerve action in extremity regeneration is that the axis cylinder emits a chemical substance which is important for the growth. Although this view does not preclude the others, it seems the most reasonable at present, since nerve fibers are known to give off chemical substances (*neurohumors* or *mediators*) important for their function. The idea that a known chemical mediator, such as acetylcholine or sympathin, serves as the nervous agent of growth has been expressed a number of times in the literature on amphibian regeneration, and, indeed, some initial experiments have already been reported (Schotté, 1926; Needham, 1952, p. 67; Taban, 1955). Some recent experiments lend substance to the thought that a chemical product of the neuron of some sort acts in regeneration. Lender (1955) has shown that regeneration of the ocelli of Planaria depends on an extractable substance of the head ganglia which can be supplied in the absence of the latter. The apparent effect of this humoral agent is to cause migration and accumulation of cells of regeneration at the wound area. Welsh (1946) in a brief report observed also in Planaria that atropine interrupts regeneration and that pilocarpine enhances it, and he concluded that the acetylcholine mechanism is a trophic mechanism as well as an impulse-mediating one.

As a first approach to the problem of the chemical nature of the nerve contribution to regeneration, my students and I embarked on an analysis of the importance of acetylcholine or its related nerve mechanisms in the new growth (preliminary report, Singer, Scheuing, and Hall, 1953). Theoretical evaluation of the problem suggested, at first, that it was unlikely that acetylcholine itself was the neural agent of growth. First of all, the action of the nerve in regeneration appears not to be related to impulse conduction or transmission, with which acetylcholine is so concerned. The nerve fiber, whether motor or sensory, always acts centrifugally in its effect on regeneration, whereas it conducts in the reverse direction in the sensory neuron. Moreover, reflex connections or any other connections with the central nervous system are not required for the trophic action because an isolated sensory supply cut from connection with the central nervous system can alone evoke the growth (Singer, 1943; review, Singer, 1952). Indeed, spinal ganglia themselves, when implanted into an otherwise denervated regenerate, will sustain growth (Anderson and Singer, unpublished). Another reason for doubting that acetylcholine is the trophic substance is the fact that sensory fibers, in contrast to motor fibers, contain very little, if any, acetylcholine (Loewi and Hellauer, 1938; Feldberg, 1954; Wolfgram, 1954), and yet they are very effective agents of growth (Singer, 1952); there is even a suggestion that the individual sensory neuron may be a more effective agent of growth than the motor one. Finally, there is little to be found in the pharmacologic literature on acetylcholine other than the above-mentioned ones on regeneration to suggest that acetylcholine can provide the growth-stimulating effect which nerves have upon regeneration.

In our pharmacologic program of analysis of the acetylcholine mechanism in limb regeneration, we subjected the regenerate to drugs of various sorts and in various ways. In most of our studies we infused solutions directly into the growth by a method especially devised for regeneration studies (Singer, 1954; Singer, Weinberg, and Sidman, 1955); in other experiments we immersed the entire animal or the stump alone in test solutions. Our results to this moment have not solved the problem of whether a substance or complex is the means by which the nerve influences regeneration. However, they have provided a detailed survey, still in progress, of the possible influence of the acetylcholine mechanism and have added some important details concerning the nature of the regeneration process. We have found that substances known to interfere with the acetylcholine mechanism also block the regeneration of fully innervated stumps. When atropine is infused for a period of 5 hours or more at a concentration of about 0.01 *M*, regeneration stops for a few days and then resumes. If the regenerate is reinfused before resumption of growth, the delay persists; and the infusions may be repeated and regeneration permanently blocked. Similar results are observed with procaine hydrochloride and tetraethylammonium hydroxide. As I have already noted, it is quite difficult to suppress regeneration even with substances ordinarily considered harmful (Singer, Weinberg, and Sidman, 1955), and so the results with these drugs are all the more striking. Consistent with the results are some others in which substances that simulate or protect the acetylcholine mechanism have no effect on regeneration even when introduced in high concentrations. Eserine salicylate in concentrations approximating saturation does not interrupt regeneration. Nor do pilocarpine nitrate, methacholine chloride, and acetylcholine chloride.

The results with drugs that affect the acetylcholine mechanism suggest, therefore, an important role of acetylcholine in regeneration. However, attempts to maintain growth of denervated regenerates with solutions of acetylcholine alone or in combination with eserine have to this point been unsuccessful. We have applied acetylcholine by repeated infusions or in other ways and under various conditions and concentrations which have been reported to favor the action of this substance but have not succeeded in duplicating the nerve action. Of course, no matter how favorably one may apply acetylcholine experimentally, one can never duplicate the conditions under which the nerve operates. The nerve pervades the growth, lies in immediate contact with the responding cells and tissues, and acts continuously. In contrast, available experimental techniques necessarily introduce important variables, such as anaesthesia, interrupted application, and variation in concentration of test substances, to mention but a few. For example, prolonged infusion requires continuous anaesthesia, but we observed that anaesthesia or other means of chronic immobilization tended to slow and suppress the growth and, after a few days, to kill the animal (Martin and Singer, unpublished). However, intermittent application of the drug was also unsatisfactory, since continuous application is required to test adequately the effect of a substance as labile as acetylcholine. Therefore, until acetylcholine can be applied to the growth in a continuous fashion approximating the generally presumed one of the nerves, conclusions concerning its role in regeneration must be reserved. Yet the fact that agents which block acetylcholine also interfere in some way with regeneration and that acetylcholine itself and agents which protect it do not themselves harm the growth is of importance in the analysis of the trophic mechanism. The results suggest that some facet of the acetylcholine mechanism may serve, even if indirectly, in the regenerative process. Perhaps some other chemical emanation is the trophic agent of the nerve, and a facet of the acetylcholine mechanism of the nerve is used in its elaboration. Or it may be that the pharmacologic blocking agents influence a mechanism of the nerve of which the production of acetylcholine is only one expression, the other being the trophic one. Perhaps acetylcholine, without being the trophic agent itself, is needed for the transport, uptake, or utilization of some more important substance from the nerves or from elsewhere. These speculations may prove to be far removed from the facts. Yet it is of interest that our results seem to relate in some way, albeit vaguely, the trophic mechanism and the mechanism of chemical mediation of the nerve impulse. Both are fundamental neuronal expressions which exist throughout animal forms, and, given the above results, it is not unreasonable to speculate that, as different as these functions are, they may be expressions that appeared in the early evolution of an important biochemical mechanism of the neuron.

4. Until recently the nerve was thought to play upon the tissue of the stump in general, and no attention was given to assigning a preferential

interaction of the nerve with one of the tissues. However, in recent years an intense interest has developed concerning the role of the epidermis in regeneration, and this interest was further heightened by the discovery of the invasion of the epidermis by numerous nerve fibers during the formative phases of regeneration (Singer, 1949*a, b*). The question then arose whether the nerve expresses itself in the regenerative process by way of a special relation to the epidermis (Singer, 1949*b;* Thornton, 1954, 1956). Because of the importance of this question today, I wish to discuss it in a separate category, although it could properly be considered in the preceding ones.

The revival of interest in recent years in the role of the epidermis in limb regeneration stemmed particularly from the work of Rose and his students (see, for example, Rose, 1948*a, b*) on the possible cellular contribution of the epidermis to the blastema. Their notion that some mesenchymatous cells arise from epidermis has not found general support, but there is agreement that the epithelial role, whatever its nature, is an essential one. The importance of the epidermis received further emphasis when massive invasion of the epidermis by nerve fibers was discovered. It is tempting to attach special significance to this somewhat unique event because of the demonstrated importance of the nerve in the phases of early regeneration, and various interpretations have been put upon the nerve-epidermal relation. The nerve might serve to govern the activity of the epidermis, whatever this activity may be (Singer, 1949*a*); as one example, the nerve may stimulate or modulate the histolytic activity which has been attributed to the epidermis (Orechowitsch and Bromley, 1934). Thornton has focused upon the fact that at the time of invasion the epidermis is quite thick, being sometimes three or four times that of normal epidermis (see, e.g., Pl. I, Fig. 2; also, in Fig. 1 compare proximal and distal epidermis). He ascribes a causal relation between the nerve invasion and the epidermal thickening and wonders whether a nerve-induced thickening might not be a precondition of limb regeneration. Goss (1956) also emphasizes the nerve invasion as a controlling mechanism of regeneration and has advanced a scheme whereby the nerve causes epithelial thickening and overgrowth and thus allows, by decreased pressure of confinement, underlying tissues to grow and enlarge and to form a regenerate.

Perhaps it is true that the physical presence of the nerve within the epidermis reflects a relation between nerve and epidermis which provides the key to subsequent events. Yet it may well be that there is no further significance to the invasion of the epidermis by the nerve than that physical and chemical conditions of the epidermis and subepidermal tissues are such in the early regenerate that nerve fibers find a ready path of invasion of the epithelium. There is no connective tissue barrier in the form of a basal membrane or other structure to bar the entrance of fibers (Pl. I, Figs. 2 and 3). Moreover, the basal epidermal cells are somewhat loosely arranged (Pl. I, Fig. 3), with obvious spaces between them (Taube, 1923; Singer, 1949*b*). The well-known regenerative powers of axis cylinders would certainly not be limited by such naked contact between epidermis and underlying tissue and such loose contact between epidermal cells. Moreover, the thickening of the epithelium may only reflect a response to underlying events and not particularly to the presence of intra-epidermal fibers. A characteristic of epidermis is that it responds readily to alterations in underlying tissues. Ordinarily, we think of the adjustment as being primarily a mechanical one, to keep pace with the area of underlying tissue, but the epidermis is also known to respond to a range of chemical and metabolic events in subepidermal tissues.

Such thoughts on the role of nervous invasion of the epidermis and of the significance of the epidermal thickening are advanced to round out our speculations on the function of nerve and epidermis in regeneration and are not meant to substitute for, or to minimize, the other and perhaps more important speculations. Indeed, it is most interesting and perhaps of prime significance in the analysis of the problem of the origin and growth of the regenerate that the activity of the two tissues to which in recent years dominant roles have been ascribed in regeneration should now be interrelated and unified into one fundamental mechanism of influence on the growth.

EXTINCTION OF REGENERATIVE CAPACITY IN PHYLOGENETIC SERIES

The influence of the nerve upon regeneration bears directly on the important problem of the decline and loss of regenerative capacity in the vertebrate series, and I wish to spend the remainder of my time reviewing the history of this problem and its present status (Singer, 1954*b*). Except for regeneration of appendages in fishes, urodele amphibians, and the larvae of anurans and of the tail and perhaps the jaw in lizards, the higher vertebrates do not regenerate these structures. The frog in its life-cycle reflects the phylogenetic limitation and loss in regenerative capacity. In the tadpole stage the limbs regenerate, but, as the animal approaches the time of metamorphosis, there is a loss in regenerative response to amputation which appears at first proximally and then sweeps distally (Singer, 1954*a*). An exception to the loss of regenerative capacity is the African clawed frog, *Xenopus laevis,* which does regenerate the amputated limb, although the growth tends to be heteromorphic and occurs less readily after proximal amputation (Beetschen, 1952).[6] Beetschen points out, as did Rostand (1932) in his brief report, that *Xenopus* is a primitive frog and that the retention of regenerative capacities is associated with its primitive character.

There have been various theories to account for the loss in regenerative capacity in the phylogenetic and ontogenetic series which need only be touched upon here, since they have been surveyed in detail elsewhere (Singer, 1954*b*). Salient among the speculations is that of increased differentiation or complexity of tissues, rendering them incapable of undergoing the changes prerequisite for regeneration. There is also the view that changes in the internal milieu or hormonal balance occur which are less conducive to regrowth. And, finally, since synchrony in regeneration of associated tissues is required to build the organ, the thought has been advanced in one form or another that there is disharmonious tissue regrowth to interfere with organ regeneration. Based on these and other various outlooks, experiments were attempted to evoke regrowth in the postmetamorphic frog or in other forms. Spallanzani was the first to raise this problem of the loss of regenerative capacity in the frog and in higher forms, and there is a suggestion in his writings (Prodromo, 1768) that he attempted in some way to evoke growth, although there is no record of such experiments: "But if the above-mentioned animals[7] . . . recover their legs . . . how comes it to pass, that other land animals . . . are not endowed with the same power? Is it to be hoped that they may acquire them by some *useful dispositions?*"[8] T. H. Morgan (1908) and others have searched for such useful dispositions but without success; and it was only in recent years that growth has been successfully recalled in the frog after the time when it is ordinarily lost. This was done first by Liosner (1931) and Polezaiev (see, for example, 1946) and then in more effective fashion by Rose (1945). The experimental means used were repeated irritation of the amputation stump with mechanical or chemical agents. The explanation which Rose advanced was that the skin ordinarily heals over too rapidly and prevents intimate and prolonged contact between the epidermis and the underlying tissue, and that this contact is prerequisite for growth. This explanation must be revised because of the information now avail-

6 The important paper of Beetschen appeared during the preparation of my work published in 1954. I regret to have missed it. In this paper Beetschen refers to the early observations of Rostand (1932) and Woodland (1920).

7 Reference to "aquatic salamanders."

8 My emphasis.

able on the nerve influence in regeneration. First of all, there is no regeneration of the traumatized amputation stump if the stump is also denervated (Singer and Kamrin, 1954). Consequently, such regenerates are evoked only against a background of nerve activity, and one wonders how it is that the nerve can now invoke growth but not without generalized irritation and inflammation. The answer is possibly to be found in certain speculations and experiments which have been advanced concerning the relation between nerve number and regenerative powers in the newt. Regeneration of the limb of the adult newt requires an adequate quantity of nerve fibers (Singer, 1946). If fewer fibers than approximately one-third of the normal supply are available at the amputation surface of the upper limb, regeneration does not occur. The individual fiber is, presumably, just as active under these circumstances, but there are not enough to accomplish the action; and so there are threshold needs which must first be satisfied. The question naturally follows whether in the course of development the available nerve supply of the frog becomes a threshold-inadequate stimulus of growth. This could occur if the responding tissues become relatively refractory to the nerve or if there is disparate proliferation of nerve and the tissue which it subserves (Singer, 1954*b*). A disparate increase in nerve number and quantity of tissue as expressed in the surface area of amputation has indeed been recently reported by Van Stone (1955), who showed that the regions of the limb first to lose regenerative capacity are those having the smallest number of nerve fibers per unit area. When the number of fibers at the amputation surface of the forelimb was increased substantially by deviation of the sciatic and its branches from the hind limb, regeneration was evoked in the postmetamorphic frog (Singer, 1954*b*). These observations show that in the frog the nerve fibers do have the quality to induce regenerative growth and that this quality is expressed when there are enough fibers available. It may be that the quantitative inadequacy of nerve fibers which occurs during development of the limb is a function not merely of disparate increase in nervous representation but also of change in tissue response to the nerve. In the case of trauma-induced regenerates, it may well be that irritation makes the tissues less refractory to the nerve, so that a previous quantitatively inadequate source now fulfils the nerve requirement and that in the nerve-induced growths the relative resistance of the tissue is overcome by the increase in nerve number. It seems probable in the study of the regenerative capacity in the anurans that, at one time in their evolution from an ancestral form common to the urodeles, the extremities of the adult were capable of regeneration, a capacity which is exhibited even today, albeit in a limited fashion, by the primitive *Xenopus*. But then regenerative powers became increasingly restricted, and the evolutionary trend is reflected today in the gradual loss during ontogenesis. However, the loss is not an irrevocable one, and it is of interest that it can be recalled by alteration—not of the hereditary substance but of the quantitative relations between tissues. Thus such a morphologic change in the relation of wound tissues is followed by a developmental expression that does not ordinarily exist in the adult.

In the light of the success in evoking regeneration in the frog, one may wonder, with the same degree of confident expectation which Spallanzani expressed in his Prodromo, whether "useful dispositions" might not now be found to induce regeneration of extremities in still higher forms and "should the flattering expectation of obtaining the advantage for ourselves be considered entirely as chimerical?" or, as T. H. Morgan wrote in 1906: ". . . for if we could determine why man does not replace a lost arm or leg, we might possibly go further and discover how such a process could be induced by artificial means. . . . I can not but think that some day this may be accomplished."

It seems appropriate that the first "useful disposition" should revolve around the nerve as a central mechanism, and it is appropriate in future attempts to invoke regrowth in still higher forms to examine the nerve mechanism further. The most fundamental physiologic characteristic of the nervous system is that it provides for the unity of the response of the animal as one integrated individual. Commensurate with this function is the fact, which now needs further emphasis, that the nervous system also provides for the morphologic unity and integrity of the individual in its action on trophic maintenance of peripheral tissues and on the regeneration of lost parts.

DISCUSSION

Discussion leader: CHARLES S. THORNTON, *Department of Biology, Kenyon College*

DR. THORNTON opened the discussion period by remarking that, among the provocative points that Dr. Singer's paper raised, the speculations concerning the possibility that the acetylcholine mechanism may occupy some facet in the nerve influence are of particular interest. It might seem paradoxical that the nerve influence is, as Schotté and Butler have demonstrated, quite necessary for the blastema to pass through what they term the "inductive phase," during which the transformation of the "accumulation blastema" into a morphologically determined regenerate occurs, since the work of Guyénot and his students has shown beyond doubt that nerves do not have specific morphogenetic activity in regeneration. However, without specifically directing the determination of the blastema, the nerves apparently provide an environment on which the processes of determination are dependent. Some of the ideas which Weiss, Tyler, Spiegel, Holtfreter, and others have expressed recently may well be of help in pointing the way to new approaches to the investigation of certain aspects of blastemal determination. Could it be, for example, that the nerve influence, mediated possibly by the activities of acetylcholine or by affecting the ionic or the immunochemical organization of the blastemal cell surfaces, is directed at intercellular relations within the blastema—changes which allow the reassortment of these naturally dissociated cells? In this respect the non-differentiating blastemata which develop on the limb stumps of anuran larvae which are in the process of losing their ability to regenerate and in which apparently the neural activity is reduced are perhaps worthy of more attention than they have yet received. One gains the impression (quantitative studies are still incomplete) from comparing these non-developing blastemata with normally differentiating ones that cellular density may play a part in blastemal cell differentiation—an intimate grouping of blastemal cells being correlated with tissue determination and differentiation. Certainly, the localized cellular condensations which precede tissue differentiation in normally regenerating limb blastemata are not observed in the anuran non-differentiating blastemata. Possibly the nerves influence the cellular density or the cellular mass of the blastema, thus affecting intercellular behavior critical to the processes of determination.

Dr. Thornton pointed out that in the larval salamander, but apparently not in the adult, excessive tissue regression follows amputation and denervation of the limb. In these limb stumps tissue dedifferentiation does not lead to the accumulation of a blastema. Rather, the cells which in the normal course of regeneration would accumulate to form the blastemal mass of cells simply disappear, somehow absorbed. If nerves do influence the intercellular relationships within the blastema in normal regeneration, could regression be a resultant of the absence of a similar neural activity? That is, dedifferentiating cells may not accumulate because specific neural agents which are somehow needed to set up mutually attractive intercellular relationships are lacking. Dispersal rather than aggregation is thus favored. It would be interesting to compare, among other approaches to this problem, the calcium distribution in denervated and in normally innervated limb stumps.

In the general discussion of Dr. Singer's paper, Dr. Goss (Brown), referring to the possibility that nerves might exert their influence by affecting a specific tissue in the limb, stated that he had carried out experiments to determine whether skin alone or cartilage formation also is so influenced. He found that regenerative inhibition of denervated limbs is attended by little or no cartilage formation. If the lower forelimb of a newt is denuded of its skin and inserted into the coelom following amputation, regeneration likewise does not occur, but amorphous masses of cartilage are produced terminally. However, when such limbs are denervated, the considerably smaller amounts of cartilage formed are commensurate with the denervated external limbs. This indicates that mesodermal tissues are affected by nerves and that this influence need not be mediated indirectly through the skin. In this respect there might well be a difference between the amphibian limb and the catfish taste barbel in which cartilage regeneration is independent of nerves.

Dr. Thornton then pointed out that the skin covering the amputation surface of a limb stump does have important inhibitory or stimulatory effects on regeneration. Thus, when the denervated limb stump of an adult newt is finally allowed to become reinnervated, the regenerative capacity of this limb is regained only after removal of the skin covering the limb tip. In this case all the stump tissues, with the one exception of the skin at the limb tip, are fully innervated, so that nerve pathways are present for the passage of the cells of regeneration. Nevertheless, cell migration fails. In experiments with larval *Amblystoma* in which limb regression was produced, by injury and denervation, to such an extent that all formed distal structures such as digits disappeared, reinnervation in most cases led to regeneration. In these larvae, although no amputation had been performed and thus no wound epithelium developed, nerve fibers penetrated the tip epidermis profusely, an apical cap formed, and regeneration proceeded normally. When, however, dense mats of dermal fibers became interposed between the tip epidermis and the regenerating nerves, no nerve fibers were able to enter the epidermis of the limb tip or even approach it. In all cases similar to this, no apical cap formed, and regeneration failed. As in the adult limb stumps, all the remaining tissues of the limb stump were richly innervated; neural pathways existed, but cell migrations failed to occur, and no blastema cell accumulation took place.

Dr. Singer commented that all students of regeneration agree that a naked contact between epidermis and the underlying mesoderm is necessary for limb regeneration to occur. However, it is not so certain that the physical presence of nerve fibers within the epidermis is required. He has found, for example, that a motor supply alone will support regeneration of a limb, and here nerve fibers are not present within the skin. He pointed out, however, that nerve fibers may need only to approach the skin and may give off stimulatory substances to it. He also agreed that if connective tissue fibers are interposed between the epidermis and the mesodermal tissues of the stump, no growth will occur, and he commented that the experiments of Rose and of Thornton in recent years have underlined the importance of the epidermis in regeneration.

· V ·

Discussion of the Paper The Role of Hormones in Regeneration

O. E. SCHOTTÉ[1]
Amherst College

Discussion leader: J. J. Kollros, *Department of Zoölogy, State University of Iowa*

Dr. Kollros commented that Dr. Schotté had emphasized the importance of the cellular responses during regeneration and that he had also done something about emphasizing the time of action and indicated the importance of very careful studies on dosage. It should be pointed out, however, that there is one thing which does not appear in these studies but which is found in some other investigations. In the regeneration of the gonopodium of certain fish, for example, the prior treatment with androgens influences the regeneration of that gonopodium even after castration and the termination of the exposure to hormone of that tissue. On the other hand, in some other fish after castration the effect of prior exposure with androgen is not felt. This is pointed out simply to emphasize that not only is there some importance to the time at which hormones may act during the course of regeneration but there may be prior experiences of tissues at the periphery which must also be considered. Dr. Schotté mentioned the work of Speidel involving the use of thyroid hormone in which exposure prior to amputation of the tail and continued exposure inhibited regeneration completely. If treatment is delayed slightly, then regeneration is greatly inhibited but not completely so, while later treatment has a stimulating or morphogenetic effect.

Dr. Kollros expressed the opinion that we should also look at various systems undergoing regeneration for the possibility of discovering periods of sensitivity, and also of insensitivity, of the same sort that we find in embryonic studies. We are, for example, all familiar with the fact that the frog embryo shows no response to thyroid hormone until it is about 8–9 mm. long (*Rana pipiens*) and that not until it is 20–25 mm. long do certain of the tissues show responses to the hormone. Some tissues become sensitive early and some late. The possibility that there are different sensitivities in the tissues of the regenerating limb and different times of onset of response has yet to be explored.

Dr. Kollros also pointed out that Dr. Schotté has stressed the inadequacy

1 [Dr. Schotté's paper had not yet been received at time of publication. The discussion is included as being of great value in itself.—Editor.]

of studies on dosage. Perhaps the problem of species specificity should also be pointed out. Some clues concerning this are found in studies on normal development or at least mildly modified development. For example, in salamanders the limb, in its initial development, is independent of the pituitary or thyroid, whereas in the frog there is dependence on the pituitary as it acts through the thyroid (but a complete independence of the pituitary if we apply the thyroid hormone alone). Also, within a given species such as *R. pipiens* we have the difference between the sensitivity of the tail and the sensitivity of the limb with respect to hormones. In *R. pipiens* the hind leg appears to be the most sensitive of the indicators of the presence of thyroid hormone. If one uses DL-thyroxine, the hind leg will respond if the tadpole is put in a solution of 0.04 μg. per liter, although very slowly, and as the dosage increases, it will respond ever more rapidly. It should be pointed out, however, that in these low concentrations, although there is a response which is visible externally, there is a stoppage point at which further development of the limb does not continue. It is the stage before the web forms, for example. Thus the results of studies of dosage problems in development may be of value in regeneration studies.

In the general discussion which followed Dr. Kollros' remarks, DR. RICHARDSON (Connecticut College) inquired of Dr. Schotté whether other hormones than the ones he mentioned might be involved. She referred to preliminary experiments in her own laboratory, in which growth hormones free of ACTH and thyrotropic factors have been used in regeneration studies. Whether the dosage used produces a stress reaction is not yet known, but a good regeneration is obtained in hypophysectomized animals treated at crucial times with the purified growth hormone.

MR. SCHMIDT (Princeton) expressed interest in the dosage that Dr. Schotté used when he obtained regeneration with an excess of ACTH. He stated that he had implanted L-thyroxine into one amputated limb of thyroidectomized newts. If the dosage was more than 1 μg., he obtained inhibition of the implanted limb but not of the amputated control limb of the other side. Dosages below 1 μg. allowed normal regeneration to occur in the implanted limb.

DR. STONE commented that, in removing the lens from the eye of a hypophysectomized newt, there is no injury to the dorsal iris, and good regeneration is obtained. Also after the iris is exposed in the hypophysectomized animal, producing a wound surface, a new iris regenerates perfectly well. Since, in the limb, the epithelium covers the wound surface as readily in the hypophysectomized animal as in the normal one and since the iris membrane is an epithelial membrane, is it not possible that perhaps the epithelium itself is not responding to a stress? DR. SCHOTTÉ replied that he thought that this was definitely the case. He found no appreciable difference in wound healing between normal and hypophysectomized newts. He does not think that the epithelium responds to stress.

· VI ·

The Effect of X-Rays on Regenerative Capacity[1]

H. A. L. TRAMPUSCH

Division of Experimental Morphology, Anatomical-embryological Laboratory, University of Amsterdam

In studying the interaction of regeneration and the effect of irradiation, we are prompted not so much by a desire to include X-rays among the immediate environmental factors—although this would by no means be merely speculative in the age of atomic energy—but rather by the fact that, of all biologically active rays, X-rays are the easiest to control and to administer in a reproducible form. We can then direct our attention to the general effect of X-rays and try to find out what biological reactions they will cause in living cells. We can also compare the behavior of regenerating tissue before and after irradiation and draw our conclusions with regard to the effect of X-rays—a method which is often adopted by pathologists studying tumors. Finally, we can investigate the regenerative process as such, use X-rays as a means of altering its course, and in this way try to approach the mechanism of both X-ray effect and regeneration. In the present paper I propose to adhere to the latter way, even though I realize its shortcomings and one-sidedness, considering the many aspects of the subject.

Confining our subject to the extremities of larval amphibians and their regenerative power, we see that a limb that is torn or cut off will in course of time be restored to its original form. This is not the case with a limb which has been exposed to X-rays prior to amputation. The effect of X-rays on a limb is rather like what we would expect in a tumor after applying a therapeutic dose: if given in the correct amount, it will completely arrest all further growth. In young specimens an apical injury or partial amputation, which would be restored and heal almost immediately in a non-irradiated limb, may result, according to Butler (1933), in gradual reduction of the stump and its eventual complete disappearance.

[1] Research supported by the Netherlands Organization for Pure Scientific Research (ZWO) and an institutional grant to the Anatomical-embryological Laboratory from the Rockefeller Foundation.

If regeneration has, however, once commenced and a blastema already been formed on the stump, irradiation may inhibit further growth without causing any regression (Butler and Puckett, 1940). Once an equilibrium has been established, the stump will remain unchanged.

As a result of these observations Butler attached special importance to the blastema, which, as he assumes, constitutes a kind of antagonistic principle to the processes which produce regression. So far, however, it has been possible neither to identify its substance nor to find out how it works.

Before even beginning to venture any conjectures on the nature of this factor, we must first realize the origin of the blastema, in which it is supposed to exist. It is necessary to know whether its material is systemic or formed locally in consequence of amputation.

As early as in the 1920's the origin of the blastema was a subject that caused much discussion, culminating in the controversy about local or hematogenous origin. Hertwig (1927), who used haploid grafts on diploid hosts, thought that in all probability the mesenchymal component of the blastema originated in the wound surface, while the epidermis migrated from the surrounding area. Hellmich (1929), on the other hand, held that the blastema was derived from elements in the blood and the perivascular connective tissue. In this controversy Butler and O'Brien (1942) produced a conclusive argument by irradiating the genual region of *Eurycea bislineata* with X-rays and then amputating the limb distally from, proximally to, or through the irradiated part. The animals always regenerated whatever portion of the limb had been amputated, except from the directly irradiated field. As only the narrow strip of irradiated tissue was unable to produce a blastema, its hematogenous origin was ruled out, and a local derivation could no longer be doubted.

If we assume a local origin of the blastema, we can concentrate our attention on a narrower field. At the same time, we can closely follow what is taking place on the surface of the wound and try to determine whether there are differences between irradiated and non-irradiated limbs. As the latter will form a blastema and the former will not, we might now consider Butler's hypothesis about the part played by the blastema and at the same time inquire into the mechanism of X-ray effects.

As stated before, a limb once exposed to irradiation is, after amputation, no longer capable of regenerating. If we observe such a stump in an axolotl of about 40 mm. (smaller, i.e., younger, animals show a tendency toward regression and are therefore less suitable for these experiments), we notice that immediately after amputation the skin and muscle first retract from the exposed end of the femur (Fig. 1); shortly after this an epidermic epithelium begins to advance over the rim of the wound, closing it in almost the same time as in a non-irradiated limb. Sections through recently closed wounds do not show any difference whether the limb was irradiated or not. Stasis and dilatation of the blood vessels, leukocytosis, and clearance of cellular debris proceed in the usual manner. While, however, in an ordinary stump, the migration of epithelium will come to an end soon after the epidermal cells have met and inter-

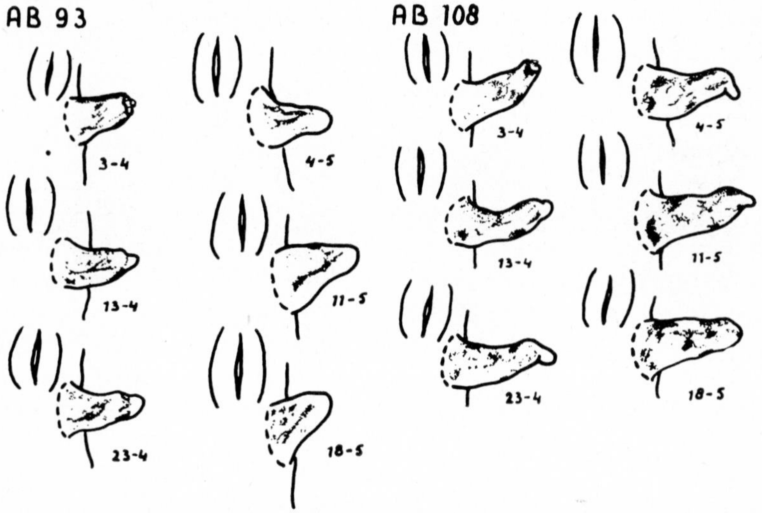

FIG. 1.—Camera lucida drawings of successive stages of irradiated limb stumps

mingled, this is by no means the case in an irradiated stump: here the migration of epithelium continues; the epidermis covering the wound and the entire limb grows thicker and thicker, although bits of apical skin are regularly sloughed off (Pl. I, *A*). This, to use a term coined by Weiss (1950), may be called a disturbed "coaptation." Otherwise, the sections of such a stump present a fairly inert picture. Besides the thick pad of terminal epithelium, which mostly contains a great many vacuolated Leydig cells, we may occasionally see considerably tortuous bundles of muscle which have become detached from their insertion and some osteoclasts in the skeleton, although, on the whole, there is little demolition of bone. Only the subdermal connective tissue gives the impression of containing smaller nuclei and more fibers than otherwise in the unirradiated limb. Nor can we make any sensational cytologic observations in the irradiated limbs. Although the stumps show fewer mitoses, those we can discern look about normal. Moreover, an occasional tripolar mitosis might also be found in non-irradiated tissue, and it is certainly no more frequent in the irradiated stumps.

At gross examination the stumps show slight changes in form, with neither considerable growth nor regression, but, as the animal continues to grow, the stump will gradually lag behind and thus seem to have shrunk (Fig. 1). This condition will remain unchanged for several months, and no regeneration occurs.

A different picture will present itself if we replace the femur of an irradiated limb by a non-irradiated humerus of the same animal, allow-

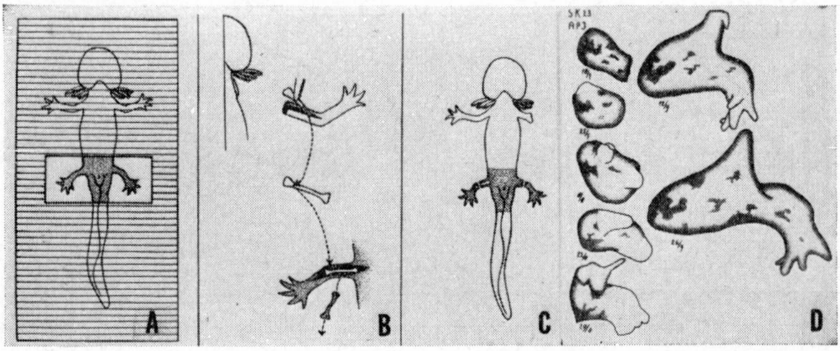

FIG. 2.—Course of experiment: *A*, irradiation through a window in a lead box; *B*, autoplastic transplantation of unirradiated skeletal tissue; *C*, amputation through level of the graft and control limb; *D*, result (case SK 23): Camera lucida drawings of successive stages of an irradiated, regenerating limb stump.

ing the implantation wound to close sufficiently, and then amputate through the implant (Fig. 2). The amputation surface will close quickly, and in about 20 days—that is considerably slower than in a non-irradiated limb—an apical blastema develops, which morphologically and histologically resembles one that regenerated normally. Somewhere along the base of the implantation wound, by then completely healed, another blastema often accumulates (Fig. 2). Sometimes the two blastemata develop separately, sometimes they merge, so that, after implantation of a bone graft, limbs regenerate in a variety of forms.

The histologic picture is characterized by intensive osteoclasia (Pl. I, *B*), followed by gradual, but in the end complete, destruction of the grafted bone. First to disappear is the bony shaft of the diaphysis. Then the matrix of the cartilage becomes refractory to stains and is eroded. Finally, the nuclei of the cells swell and assume a granulated aspect. At the later stages of the process similar cells are seen free and outside the cartilage matrix. From this an identity may be inferred between the two. Other histologic criteria correspond so completely with those of normal regeneration that elaboration would seem superfluous. Apparently, the bone graft has completely offset the effect of irradiation, thereby restoring the power of regeneration.

The surprising results of these experiments admit of several interpretations. First of all should be considered the possibility of complete dedifferentiation, followed by reconstitution from the implanted, nonirradiated tissue. Such a process, however, would imply complete metaplasia, as muscle, epidermis, etc., would have to be derived from bone and cartilage cells. Although such an explanation should not be precluded, it would, at the present stage of our knowledge, seem too bold. It may therefore be advisable to look for alternative explanations.

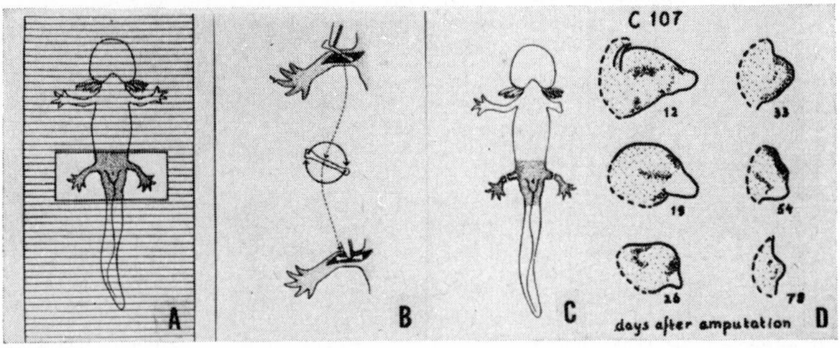

FIG. 3.—Course of experiment: *A*, irradiation through a window in a lead box; *B*, reimplantation of the rotated femur; *C*, amputation of experimental and control limb; *D*, result (case C 107): Camera lucida drawings of successive stages of an irradiated, regressing limb stump.

Polezajew (1939) once showed that the hind legs of tadpoles which were too old to regenerate spontaneously might be stimulated to regeneration by traumatizing the stumps. The surgical trauma caused by the grafted bone in our experiments might have been severe enough to start regeneration again, in spite of irradiation.

An experiment carried out on 35 axolotls was intended to test Polezajew's assumption, in that the irradiated, distoproximally rotated femur was reimplanted (Fig. 3). After amputation the wound healed normally, but the activity of the osteoclasts was such that after about 10 days the graft completely broke down. Simultaneously, histolysis began in the other tissues of the stump, changing it within 38–54 days into a miserable remnant (Fig. 3). The severe traumatization of the tissue had not caused regeneration but, on the contrary, a complete regression of the stump.

One might also associate the restoration of regenerative power with a reactivating influence emanating from the graft, possibly in connection with its breakdown. Such an influence, which might be expected to be humoral, would have to spread among the cells through diffusion, thus returning to them some factors eliminated by the previous irradiation. In this case, however, the effect of the humoral factor would have to be perceptible at some distance from the graft. Consequently, in an irradiated limb with a non-irradiated bone, regeneration would occur even if afterward the limb was amputated *distally* from the graft (Fig. 4).

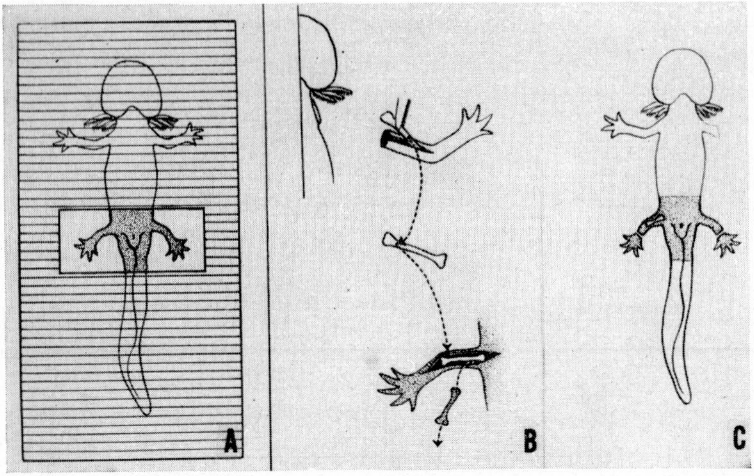

FIG. 4.—Course of experiment: *A*, irradiation through a window in a lead box; *B*, autoplastic transplantation of unirradiated skeletal tissue; *C*, amputation distally from the graft and control limb.

Of the 55 animals used, 29 were observed until 90 days after amputation. In the beginning, wound closure proceeded as described in previous series, as did the attack of osteoclasts on the graft. Besides, we can now see how the epithelium of the wound is vainly striving to regain its equilibrium (Pl. I, *C*). It proliferates freely toward the apex, piles up at the amputation surface, and shows signs of progressive degeneration. Gradually, wartlike outgrowths of the skin arise, hang down from the stumps like shreddy flaps, and are cast off at intervals. Instead of a blastema, a fibrous scar tissue develops at the site of amputation. It contains only few cells and shows no indication of regeneration. Eventually, the histologic picture shows signs of histolysis in the distal part. But, proximally, on the original implantation site at the base of the stump, cells accumulate into a blastema, which eventually, whether through active development or as a result of the regression of the distal parts, reaches the tip of the stump. Finally, all surviving animals regenerate proximally and produce incomplete limbs with a maximum of three toes.

These results suggest a possible reactivating factor in the graft, which, however, if effective, does not act by remote diffusion but only by direct contact. Nor is every kind of tissue equally susceptible to its influence. There is hardly any reaction from those muscles in which the bone graft is located. But wherever the graft comes close to the skin, either in consequence of its position in the limb or through retraction of the soft parts after amputation, that skin becomes activated. In this way, guided by the limb's epithelium, the process of regeneration is reestablished.

If the epidermis really interferes with the course of regeneration, then substitution of non-irradiated skin for the irradiated one must result in an even better neutralization of the effect of X-rays. Actually, preliminary experiments (Trampusch, 1951) have demonstrated that transplantation of non-irradiated skin of the limb restores regeneration and produces the best and most completely regenerated extremities. In order to delve deeper into the problem and to distinguish the material of the graft from that of the host, we later performed alleloplastic transplantations, by grafting the skin of black axolotls onto limbs of albinotic hosts (Fig. 5).

The non-irradiated graft soon "took" on the stripped extremity, which 1 week later was amputated across the transplant in order to bring about regeneration. Within 21–28 days a blastema of a somewhat lighter pigmentation developed (Fig. 6) that gradually flattened out into a toe plate. Although the regenerated part of the limb always remained slightly lighter than the grafted skin, it turned in the long run into a typical black. But besides black limbs, there developed, curiously enough, some entirely white ones (Fig. 7). Camera lucida drawings, made in the course of the experiment, clearly show how the graft first moved apically over the stump and gradually disappeared. Before its disappearance, however, the graft had influenced the host's tissue in such a way that it became once more capable of spontaneous regeneration in spite of irradiation. This, then, demonstrates *ad oculos* a reactivation of regenerative power. Out of 111 surviving animals, 81 produced an entirely black (color of graft!) limb, 3 an entirely white one, 1 single animal had a speckled limb; 26 grafts did not "take" and so did not cause regeneration at all.

Not only is the transplanted, non-irradiated skin of the limb subject

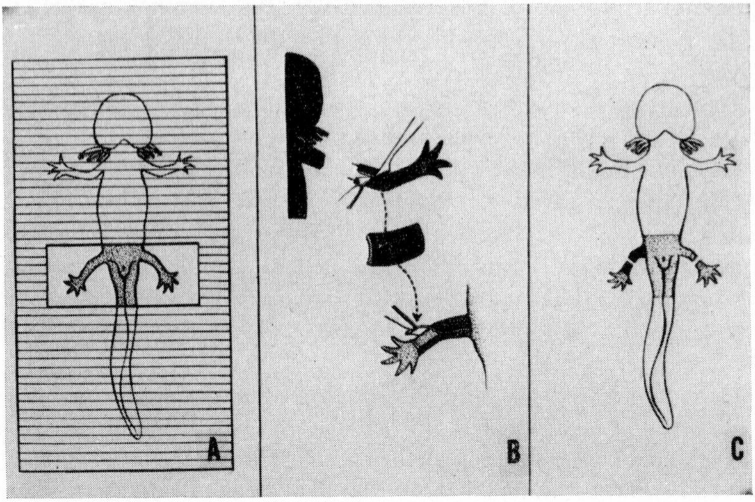

FIG. 5.—Course of experiment: *A*, irradiation through a window in a lead box; *B*, alleloplastic transplantation of unirradiated skin; *C*, amputation of experimental and control limb.

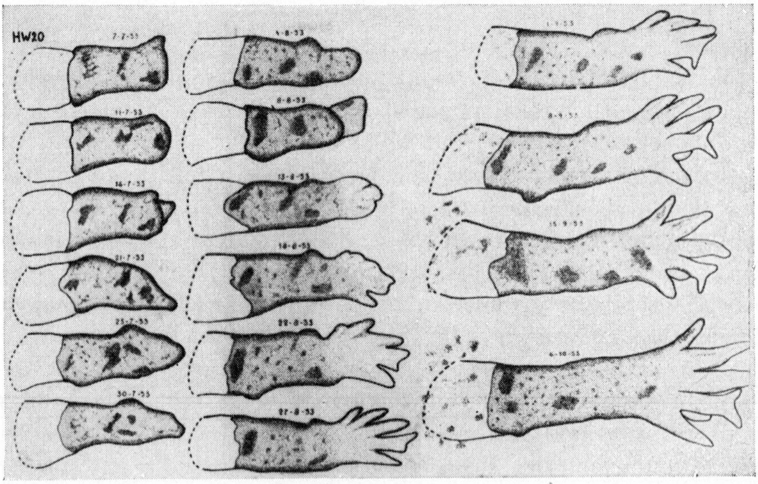

FIG. 6.—Camera lucida drawings of successive stages of an irradiated limb stump, regenerating after being covered with unirradiated skin. Example of a black regenerate.

to undisturbed "coaptation," but it also brings back the original power of regeneration into the host's tissue, producing a regenerate that contains grafted tissue as well as tissue from the host to a varying amount. The regenerated limb, therefore, may be either black or white; in the case of the speckled one the remaining implant was apparently not sufficient to color the regenerate completely.

In nearly all cases where the graft "took," the transplanted skin of the limb showed its reactivating effect on regeneration. The same does

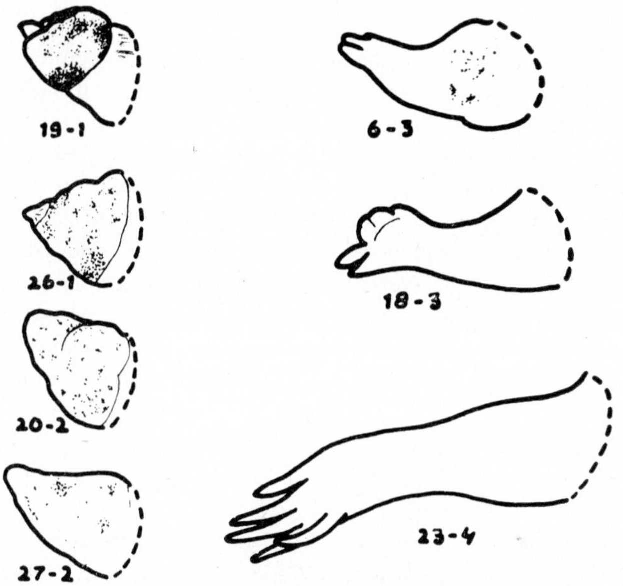

FIG. 7.—Camera lucida drawings of successive stages of an irradiated limb stump, regenerating after being covered with unirradiated skin. Example of a white regenerate.

not apply to other skin grafts. If we transplant non-irradiated skin from the belly of an axolotl onto an irradiated limb, there will be no proper regeneration, even if a normal closure of the wound occurs. Apparently, the "coaptation" of the transplant runs a similar course on the limb as it does on the body and is therefore incongruous with its location. Irrespective of the region from which the graft was taken, we see only occasionally an abortive attempt at regeneration. Most limbs show little change, some even regression. The transplanted body skin is just capable of maintaining the existing state of the stump but cannot transform it into regeneration.

Skin grafts taken from the tail cause a different reaction. When wrapped around an irradiated hind leg, skin from tail or fin usually heals quite readily and "takes" without any trouble. Amputation through such a limb also causes the epidermis to migrate in an apical direction; but nevertheless the wound does not close for several days. Meanwhile, the epithelium piles up around the protruding end of the bone, forming humps and bumps (Pl. II, *A*), which, after some time, unite (Pl. II, *B*). But even after closure of the wound the marked tendency of the epithelium to grow and migrate is not reduced, the apical skin folds merge, growing steadily larger, while apically the epithelium becomes more and more lifted from the underlying tissue (Pl. II, *C*). In the space thus formed, connective tissue begins to collect, gradually becoming loose and turgescent (Pl. II, *D*). Instead of assuming the slender, usually tapering form of a regenerating limb, the extremity under observation becomes broad and lobed and eventually develops into a boneless tail with a high, projecting fin (Fig. 8). The character of a caudal fin was unmistakable, both morphologically and histologically, in 13 out of 34 surviving animals; in 3 others the fin contained rudimentary skeletal elements, thus becoming a queer mixture of fin and leg. (The number of regressing leg stumps was particularly large after transplantation of skin from the fin, due to the jelly-like connective tissue inside, which counteracts "taking.") This series of experiments demonstrates that skin obtained from the tail, unlike body skin, could start regeneration of an irradiated stump but, at the same time, would mark the regenerate as its offspring.

Though these experiments raise more questions than they answer, they are beginning to reveal a still deficient mosaic, whose pieces are gradually falling into place. Its general outlines seem to indicate that, as a reaction to injury or terminal amputation of a limb, the epidermis begins to migrate in an apical direction, a migration which can be stopped only by coaptative forces. If the coaptation is successful, all successive stages of the regenerative process are gone through—a blastema, a toe plate, and eventually a complete limb arrive. As an effect of irradiation coaptative relations in the epithelium of the skin are disturbed, thus preventing restoration of equilibrium in the tissue systems and the development of a blastema. Direct contact with any kind of non-irradiated tissue (we tested bone, muscle, and nerve tissue) revives the coaptative power of the epidermis and restores its function in the process of regeneration, which then runs a course similar to that in a non-irradiated limb.

We have also seen that the various areas of skin in the body show a typical and specific pattern of coaptation, determining whether or not regeneration will take place. Existing structures may be involuted or

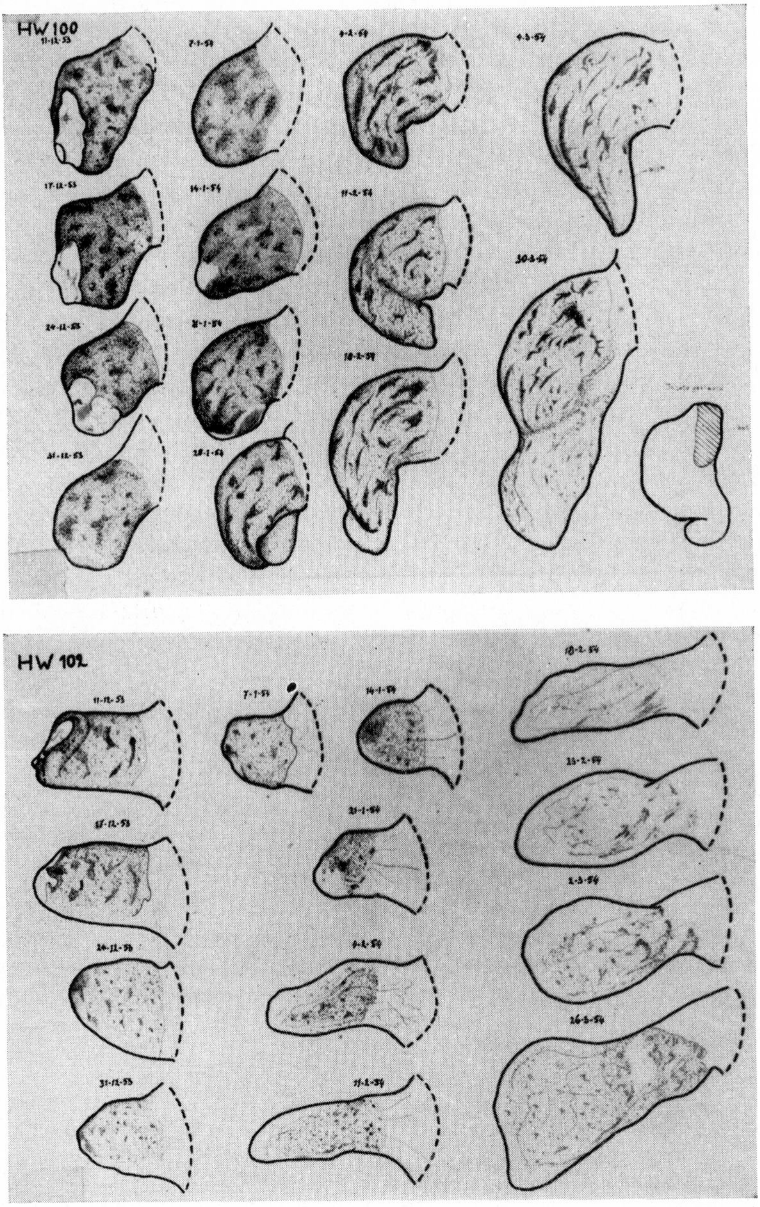

FIG. 8.—Camera lucida drawings of successive stages of irradiated limb stumps, regenerating into tail-like structures after being covered with unirradiated skin of a tail.

remodeled during the process, all this being determined by the graft and its intrinsic specificity.

With regard to the blastema and its inherent factor, the foregoing has shown unequivocally that its development as such is of little importance. A blastema is just a phase, which happens to be morphologically perceptible, though even reversible—a link in a physiologic process, whose successive stages are governed by their own automatism. The blastema is neither the beginning nor a decisive phase in the process. Time and again growths develop—especially in regressing stumps—which closely resemble a blastema, without ever producing regenerates. The "blastemic factor" which Butler missed in irradiated stumps may, as I tried to show, be reintroduced by any non-irradiated tissue and may be less important than it was once thought to be.

On the other hand, attention will to a greater extent have to be focused on the mechanism of coaptative equilibrium, regardless of whether it results from surface constitution, enzymatic or antibody-antigen systems, whether it goes back to Weiss's concept of molecular ecology with matching macromolecules, or whatever other causes there may be. We shall also have to pay more attention to the interplay between wound factors and coaptation, the more so as they are both important in initiating the process of regeneration. Experiments directed at this problem by Chiakulas (1952), Lash (1955), and others, as well as related studies by Needham (1941), Thornton (1949–51), and Tuchmann-Duplessis (1950) have shown promising aspects. They prove that further investigations in this direction may well be undertaken.

DISCUSSION

Discussion leader: E. G. BUTLER, *Department of Biology, Princeton University*

DR. BUTLER opened the discussion by commenting that in his opinion the main point which the experiments of Dr. Trampusch bring out so beautifully is the fact that we are dealing, in the case of the limb, with a "regenerating system" in which significant interactions are taking place among the various tissues, structures, and areas of the distal end of the limb after amputation. It is of particular interest that Dr. Trampusch has found that the skin may well play the most important role. It was long thought that after irradiation with ionizing radiations the urodele limb completely loses its ability to regenerate. Dr. Trampusch has now shown that this is not necessarily true. If the limb is provided, as he has demonstrated, with various unirradiated tissues, it can regain the capacity to regenerate; and particularly is this the case if it is provided with unirradiated skin from the limb. It is important to remember that irradiated tissues take part in the formation of such regenerates. Here we have a very important interaction among the tissues which emphasizes particularly the influence of the epidermis. In this connection may be mentioned the work of Thornton, which shows that in urodele larvae the point of blastema formation is apparently the point where the epidermis has been disturbed in one way or another—the point where the thickened epidermal cap forms. In some of Thornton's experiments the epidermal cap formed in an excentric position, and in such cases the blastema formed under this. DR. BUTLER further pointed out that, in recent unpublished experiments he has performed with Dr. H. F. Blum, one of the immediate effects of a single localized dosage of ultraviolet light in the urodele limb is a disturbance of the epidermis—in fact, the epidermis sloughs off, and then new epidermis migrates into the irradiated area, where it forms a thickening. Here a supernumerary limb is established. This result may lend further emphasis to the importance of the epidermis.

DR. BUTLER concluded that in the past we may have overemphasized the importance of the blastema. As Dr. Trampusch asserts, it is a phase, a part of a "regenerating system" which involves certainly a very complex interplay among the tissues at the site of amputation. It is a "system," moreover, which is mediated by nerve activity and by hormonal influences.

DR. BRUNST then inquired as to the dosage which was used in Dr. Trampusch's irradiation studies. He felt that 1,000 r is an insufficient dosage to prevent tissue regeneration. DR. TRAMPUSCH, however, pointed to the fact that every animal had both hind limbs irradiated—one received the transplant, while the other served as the control. In several hundred cases he has found that 1,000 r was absolutely sufficient to inhibit limb regeneration.

DR. STONE expressed interest in the experiment involving lack of regeneration when body skin was grafted to the irradiated limb. Was there a difference in the amount of subdermal tissue in this body skin as compared with that of the tail and limb? DR. TRAMPUSCH replied that the skin of the body is thicker, in both its epithelium and its dermis, than is that of the limb and that this might be a cause of the difference in reaction.

DR. SPEIDEL (Virginia) inquired as to the effect of the irradiation on the histology of skin. DR. TRAMPUSCH stated that he has kept series of animals for a year and has periodically fixed one limb for study. The thickness of the epidermis continues to grow for months. After some months the dermis exhibits thickening, and finally there is a rather extensive deterioration of the epithelium.

DR. SINGER expressed interest in the experiment in which regeneration was called forth in irradiated limb stumps by means of an unirradiated nerve. He mentioned similar results obtained in his own laboratory. He asked Dr. Trampusch if he believed that there was an interaction between nerves and the epidermis in recalling regeneration, and, if so, would he consider that this mechanism was involved with any implanted, non-irradiated tissue. DR. TRAMPUSCH remarked that anything which he might say should be regarded as highly speculative but that he did visualize a chain of reaction involving both the nerves and the epidermis. Each has an important part to play in this mechanism, and if these two tissues co-operate, regeneration results; if, on the other hand, they fail to work together, then the whole mechanism is stopped. DR. SINGER then remarked that, from the evidence of Dr. Trampusch's slides, the irradiated epidermis seemed greatly disrupted and there was the suggestion at least of histolysis. Would implanted non-irradiated tissue prevent this histolysis and allow a blastema to form? DR. TRAMPUSCH replied that this seemed to be the case.

Dr. Chalkley described experiments performed by one of his students which involved the exposure of the limb of the newt to 15,000 r of X-radiation. A turntable was used to insure uniformity of exposure. Nevertheless, mitoses were still observable in the connective tissues, although limb regeneration itself was inhibited.

Dr. Thornton remarked that, in respect to the co-operation between the epidermis and nerves, he had found that the stimulus for limb regeneration in larval *Amblystoma* was strongly correlated with a mitotically proliferating epidermal cap. Limb regeneration could be inhibited in *A. tigrinum* by daily removal of the wound epithelium, which, after 24 hours, had not entered on the proliferative phase. Daily removal of the wound epithelium in *A. punctatum,* however, failed to prevent regeneration. In these animals the wound epithelium became mitotically active within 12 hours after the previous removal of wound epithelium and at this time formed an apical cap.

PLATE I

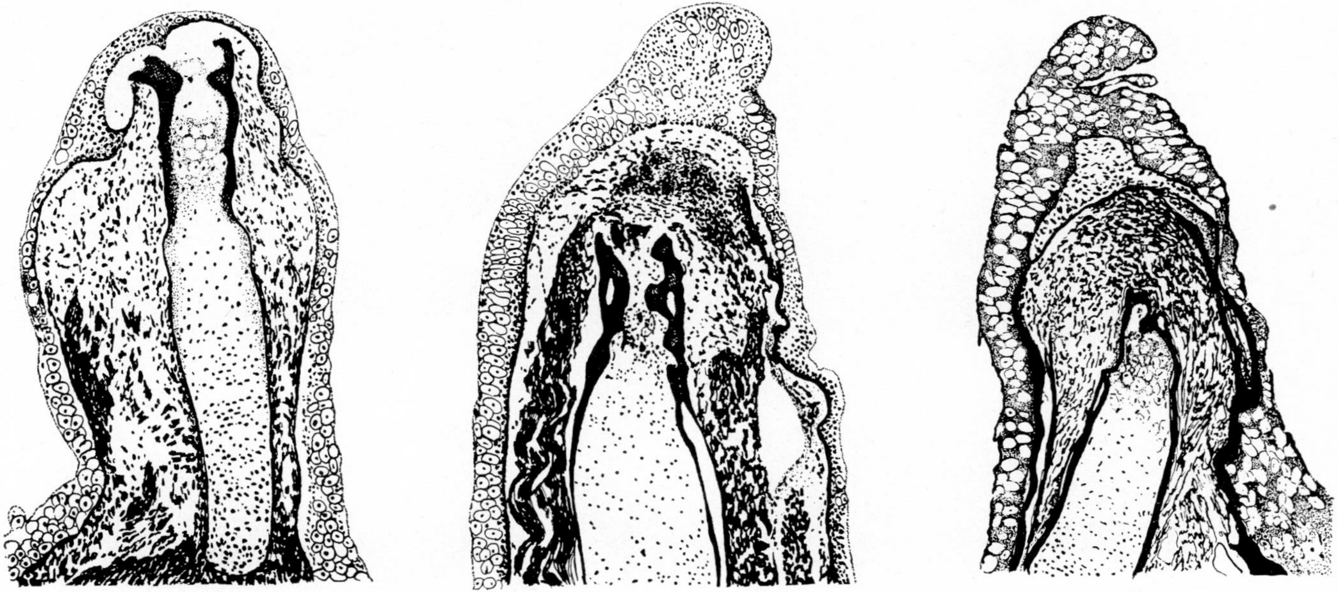

A *B* *C*

Sections showing epidermal coaptation in irradiated limb stumps amputated through the genual region.

A, Disturbed coaptation in the epithelium of an irradiated limb stump. The migrating epithilium piles up and is cast off at the apical end of the stump.

B, Re-established coaptation after implantation of unirradiated skeletal tissue in an irradiated limb. The implant is attacked by numerous osteoclasts.

C, Coaptation is not re-established after implantation of unirradiated skeletal tissue, when the implant does not reach the amputation surface. A many-layered epithelium seals the wound without permitting regeneration.

PLATE II

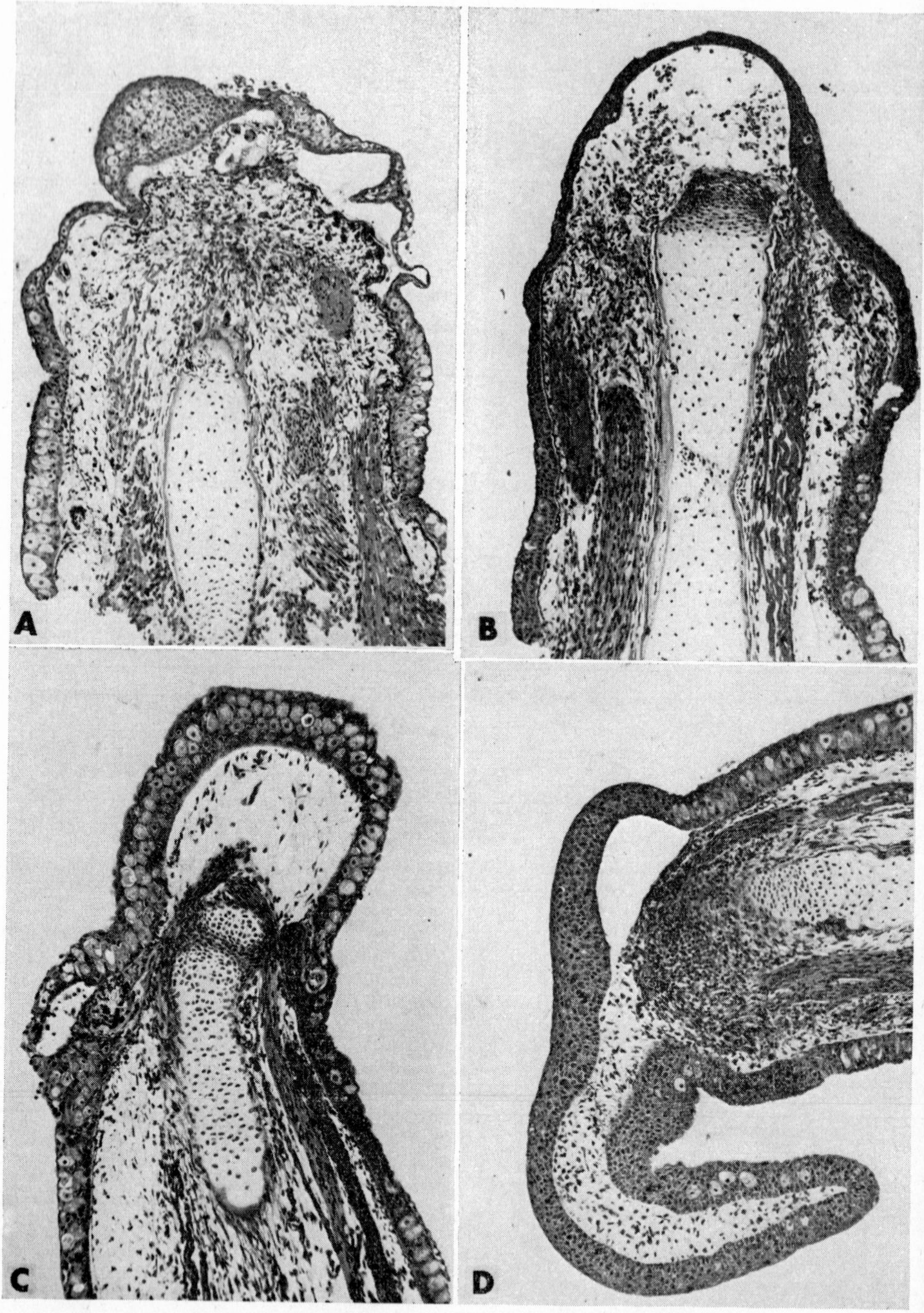

Sections through irradiated limb stumps covered by unirradiated skin from the tail.

A, The amputation wound is not yet closed, but some of the epidermal thickenings unite.

B, The epidermis is closed and lifted from the stump of the femur. Note the apical accumulation of loose connective tissue.

C, The formation of a tail fin has commenced.

D, A tail fin on the limb stump is fully developed.

References

REFERENCES FOR PAPER I (STONE)

COLUCCI, V. 1891. Sulla rigenerazione parziale dell'occhio nei Tritoni. Istogenesi e svilluppo. Studio sperimentale. Mem. ric. Accad. sci. inst. Bologna, Ser. 5, **1**:593–629.

FROHMAN, C. E., and KINSEY, V. E. 1952. Studies on the crystalline lens. V. Distribution of various phosphate-containing compounds and its significance with respect to energetics. A.M.A. Arch. Ophth., **48**:12–18.

KINSEY, V. E., and MERRIAM, F. C., 1950. Studies on the crystalline lens. II. Synthesis of glutathione in the normal and cataractous rabbit lens. A.M.A. Arch. Ophth., **44**:370–80.

MERRIAM, F. C., and KINSEY, V. E. 1950*a*. Studies on the crystalline lens. I. Technic for in vitro culture of crystalline lenses and observations on metabolism of the lens. A.M.A. Arch. Ophth., **43**:979–88.

———. 1950*b*. Studies on the crystalline lens. III. Incorporation of glycine and serine in the proteins of lenses cultured in vitro. *Ibid.*, **44**:651–58.

REYER, R. W. 1954. Regeneration of the lens in the amphibian eye. Quart. Rev. Biol., **29**:1–46.

SATO, T. 1951. Über die linsenbildende Fähigkeit des Pigmentepithels bei *Diemyctylus pyrrhogaster*. I. Pigmentepithel aus dorsalem Augunbereich. Embryologia, **1**:21–57.

———. 1953. Über die Ursachen des Ausbleibens der Linsenregeneration und zugleich über die linsenbildende Fähigkeit des Pigmentepithels bei den Anuren. Arch. f. Entw.-Mech., **146**:487–514.

SCHOTTÉ, O. E. 1953. The role of the pituitary, of ACTH, and of some adrenocortical extracts in the regeneration of limbs in adult *Triturus*. Anat. Rec., **117**:575–76.

SCHOTTÉ, O. E., and BONNEVILLE, M. A. 1955. The systemic effects of injury and of repair within dehumerized limbs of hypophysectomized *Triturus viridescens*. Anat. Rec., **121**:364.

SCHOTTÉ, O. E., and CHAMBERLAIN, J. L. 1955. Effects of ACTH upon limb regeneration in normal and in hypophysectomized *Triturus viridescens*. Rev. suisse zool., **62**: No. 15, 253–79.

SCHOTTÉ, O. E., and LINDBERG, D. A. B. 1954. Effect of xenoplastic adrenal transplants upon limb regeneration in normal and hypophysectomized newts (*Triturus viridescens*). Proc. Soc. Exper. Biol. & Med., **87**:26–29.

SCHOTTÉ, O. E., and MURPHY, G. W. 1953. Regeneration of the lens in absence of the pituitary in the adult newt (*Triturus viridescens*). J. Morphol., **93**: 447–64.

SPEMANN, H. 1905. Über Linsenbildung nach experimenteller Entfernung der primären Linsenbildungszellen. Zool. Anz., **28**:419–32.

Stone, L. S. 1944. Functional polarization in retinal development and its reestablishment in regenerating retinae of rotated grafted eyes. Proc. Soc. Exper. Biol. & Med., **57**:13–14.

———. 1947. Return of vision and functional polarization in the retinae of transplanted eyes. (Doyne Memorial Lecture, Oxford Ophthalmological Congress, 1947.) Tr. Ophth. Soc. United Kingdom, **67**:349–68.

———. 1950*a*. Development of normal and reversed vision in transplanted eyes. Acta XVI Concilium Ophth. (Britannia), pp. 644–48.

———. 1950*b*. Neural retina degeneration followed by regeneration from surviving retinal pigment cells in grafted adult salamander eyes. Anat. Rec., **106**:89–110.

———. 1950*c*. The role of retinal pigment cells in regenerating neural retinae of adult salamander eyes. J. Exper. Zoöl., **113**:9–32.

———. 1952. An experimental study of the inhibition and release of lens regeneration in adult eyes of *Triturus viridescens viridescens*. *Ibid.*, **121**: 181–224.

———. 1953. An experimental analysis of lens regeneration. Am. J. Ophth., **36**:31–39.

———. 1954*a*. Further experiments on lens regeneration in eyes of the adult newt *Triturus v. viridescens*. Anat. Rec., **120**:599–624.

———. 1954*b*. Lens regeneration in secondary pupils experimentally produced in eyes of the adult newt, *Triturus v. viridescens*. J. Exper. Zoöl., **127**:463–92.

———. 1955. Regeneration of the iris and lens from retina pigment cells in adult newt eyes. *Ibid.*, **129**:505–34.

Stone, L. S., and Griffith, B. H. 1954. Regeneration of the iris and lens in eyes of adult *Triturus v. viridescens*. J. Exper. Zoöl., **127**:153–80.

Stone, L. S., and Sapir, P. 1940. Experimental studies on the regeneration of the lens in the eye of anurans, urodeles, and fishes, J. Exper. Zoöl., **85**: 77–101.

Stone, L. S., and Steinitz, H. 1953*a*. The regeneration of lenses in eyes with intact and regenerating retina in adult *Triturus v. viridescens*. J. Exper. Zoöl., **124**:435–68.

———. 1953*b*. Effects of hypophysectomy and thyroidectomy on lens and retina regeneration in the adult newt, *Triturus v. viridescens*. *Ibid.*, pp. 469–504.

Stone, L. S., and Vultee, J. H. 1949. Inhibition and release of lens regeneration in the dorsal iris of *Triturus v. viridescens*. Anat. Rec., **103**:144–45.

ten Cate, G., and van Doorenmaalen, W. J. 1950. Analysis of the development of the eye-lens in chicken and frog embryos by means of the precipitin reaction. Proc. k. nederl. Akad. wetensch. **53**:1–18.

Wachs, H. 1914. Neue Versuche zur Wolff'schen Linsenregeneration. Arch. f. Entw.-Mech., **39**:384–451.

Woerdeman, M. W. 1953. The differentiation of the crystalline lens. J. Embryol. & Exper. Morphol., **1**:301–5.

Zalokar, M. 1944. Contribution à l'étude de la régénération du cristallin chez le *Triton*. Rev. suisse zool., **51**: No. 26, 443–521.

Zuidweg, M. H. J. 1954. Quantitative determination of the α-crystallin fraction of the eye lenses of chick embryos in various stages of development. Proc. k. nederl. Akad. wetensch., Ser. C. **57**:115–27.

REFERENCES FOR PAPER II (HOLTZER)

AVERY, G., CHOW, M., and HOLTZER, H. 1955. Comparison of the salamander and chick notochords in the differentiation of somitic tissues. Anat. Rec., **122**:444.

———. 1956. An experimental analysis of the development of the spinal column. V. Reactivity of chick somites. J. Exper. Zoöl., **132**:409–28.

BARFURTH, D. 1891. Zur Regeneration der Gewebe. Arch. micr. Anat., **37**: 406–91.

COONS, A., CREECH, H., JONES, R., and BERLINER, E. 1942. The demonstration of pneumoccocal antigens in tissues by the use of fluorescent antibody. J. Immunol., **45**:159–70.

COONS, A., and KAPLAN, M. 1950. Localization of antigen in tissue cells. J. Exper. Med., **91**:1–14.

EBERT, J. 1953. An analysis of the synthesis and distribution of the contractile protein, myosin, in the development of the heart. Proc. Nat. Acad. Sc., **39**:333–44.

GLADE, R. 1957. The effects of tail tissue on limb regeneration in *Triturus viridescens*. J. Morphol., **101**:477–522.

GROBSTEIN, C. 1956. Trans-filter induction of tubules in mouse metanephrogenic mesenchyme. Exper. Cell Res., **10**:424–40.

GROBSTEIN, C., and HOLTZER, H. 1955. In vitro studies of cartilage induction in mouse somite mesoderm. J. Exper. Zoöl., **128**:333–57.

GROBSTEIN, C., and PARKER, G. 1954. In vitro induction of cartilage in mouse somite mesoderm by embryonic spinal cord. Proc. Soc. Exper. Biol. & Med., **85**:477–80.

HADORN, E. 1952. Experimentelle bewirkte Blockierung der histologischen Differenzierung in der Chorda von Triton. Arch. f. Entw.-Mech., **144**: 491–520.

HOLTZER, H. 1951. Morphogenetic influence of the spinal cord on the axial skeleton and musculature. Anat. Rec., **109**:113–14.

———. 1952*a*. Reconstitution of the urodele spinal cord following unilateral ablation. J. Exper. Zoöl., **119**:263–302.

———. 1952*b*. Response of procartilage cells to size variations of the spinal cord. *Ibid.*, **121**:121–49.

———. 1952*c*. The dispensability of the notochord. *Ibid.*, pp. 573–92.

HOLTZER, H. 1958. Lack of organ determining activity of skin during regeneration. Anat. Rec., **132**:455.

HOLTZER, H., ABBOTT, J., and CAVANAUGH, M. 1959. Some properties of embryonic myoblasts. Exper. Cell Res., Jan. issue (in press).

HOLTZER, H., ABBOTT, J., and LASH, J. 1958. On the formation of multinucleated myotubes. Anat. Rec., **131**:567.

HOLTZER, H., AVERY, G., and HOLTZER, S. 1954. Some properties of the regenerating limb blastema cells of salamanders. Biol. Bull., **107**:313.

HOLTZER, H., and DETWILER, S. 1953. Induction of skeletogenous cells. J. Exper. Zoöl., **123**:335–60.

———. 1954. The dependence of somitic differentiation on the neural axis. Anat. Rec., **118**:390.

HOLTZER, H., HOLTZER, S., and AVERY, G. 1955. Morphogenesis of tail vertebrae during regeneration. J. Morphol., **96**:145–71.

HOLTZER, H., LASH, J., and HOLTZER, S. 1956. The enhancement of somitic muscle maturation by the embryonic spinal cord. Biol. Bull., **111**:303.

HOLTZER, H., MARSHALL, J., and FINCK, H. 1957. An analysis of myogenesis by the use of fluorescent antimyosin. J. Biophys. & Biochem. Cytol., **3**: 705–24.

HOLTZER, S. 1954. The inductive role of the spinal cord in tail regeneration in the salamander. Biol. Bull., **107**:313.

———. 1956. The inductive activity of the spinal cord in urodele tail regeneration. J. Morphol., **99**:1–40.

LASH, J., HOLTZER, H., and SWIFT, H. 1957. Regeneration of mature skeletal muscle. Anat. Rec., **128**:679–98.

LASH, J., SWIFT, H., and HOLTZER, H. 1956. Regeneration in mature striated muscle. Anat. Rec., **124**:324.

LIOSNER, L. 1941. On the formation of caudal skeleton as studied by transplantation. C. R. (Doklady) Acad. Sc., URSS, **31**:815–17.

MARSHALL, J. 1951. Localization of adrenocorticotropic hormone by histochemical and immunochemical methods. J. Exper. Med., **94**:21–30.

———. 1954. Distribution of chymotrypsinogen, procarboxypeptidase, desoxyribonuclease and ribonuclease in bovine pancreas. Exper. Cell Res., **6**:240–42.

MOMMAERTS, W., and PARRISH, R. 1951. Studies on myosin. I. Preparation and criteria of purity. J. Biol. Chem., **188**:545–52.

NEWTH, D. 1958. On regeneration after amputation of abnormal structures. J. Embryol. & Exper. Morphol., **6**:297–307.

SMITHBERG, M. 1954. The origin and development of the tail in the frog. J. Exper. Zoöl., **127**:397–426.

SPRATT, N. 1955. Analysis of the organizer center in the early chick embryo. I. Localization of prospective notochord and somite cells. J. Exper. Zoöl., **128**:121–64.

STEFANELLI, A., and CAPRIATA, A. 1944. La Rigenerazione del midello spinale nella coda rigenerata dei Tritoni. Ric. di morfol.

STRUDEL, G. 1953. L'Influence morphogène du tube nerveux sur la différenciation de la colonne vértébrale. Compt. rend. Soc. biol., **168**:132.

WATTERSON, R. 1952. Neural tube extirpation in *Fundulus heteroclitus* and resultant neural arch defects. Biol. Bull., **103**:367.

WATTERSON, R., FOWLER, I., and FOWLER, B. 1954. The role of the neural tube and notochord in development of the axial skeleton of the chick. Am. J. Anat., **95**:337–400.

WORONZOWA, M. 1939. The regeneration potencies of the tail muscles in *Amblystoma*. Bull. Biol. Med. Exper. (Russian), **8**:227–30.

ZWILLING, E. 1955. Ectoderm-mesoderm relationship in the development of the chick embryo limb bud. J. Exper. Zoöl., **128**:423–38.

REFERENCES FOR PAPER III (CHALKLEY)

BASSETT, C. A. L., EVANS, V. J., CAMPBELL, D. H., and EARLE, W. R. 1955. Characteristics and potentials of long-term cultures of human skin. Nav. M. Res. Inst., **13**:509.

BASSINA, J. A. 1940. An inquiry into regeneration by the method of calculating mitotic coefficients. Bull. Exper. Biol. Meditsny., **10**:389 (in Russian).

BRUNST, V. V., and CHÉRÉMETIÉVA, E. A. 1935. Recherches sur l'influence des

rayons X sur la régénération de la queue du Triton après une seule irradiation à doses variées. Arch. biol., **46**:357.
———. 1936. Sur la perte locale du pouvoir régénérateur chez le Triton. Arch. zool. exper. génét., **78**:56.
BUTLER, E. G. 1933. The effects of X-radiation on the regeneration of the forelimb of *Amblystoma* larvae. J. Exper. Zoöl., **65**:271.
———. 1935. Studies on limb regeneration in x-rayed *Amblystoma* larvae. Anat. Rec., **62**:295.
BUTLER, E. G., and O'BRIEN, J. P. 1942. Effects of localized X-irradiation on regeneration of the urodele limb. Anat. Rec., **84**:407.
CHALKLEY, D. T. 1954. A quantitative histological analysis of forelimb regeneration in *Triturus viridescens*. J. Morphol., **94**:21.
CLARK, E. L. 1912. Further observations on living, growing lymphatics. Their relations to the mesenchyme cells. Am. J. Anat., **13**:351.
COLUCCI, VINCENSO, 1884. Introno alla rigenerazione degli arti e della coda nei Tritoni. Studio sperimentale. Mem. ric. Accad. sc. Inst. Bologna, Ser. 4, **6**:501.
DETTELBACH, H. R. 1952. Histostatic and cytostatic effects of some aminoketones upon tail regeneration in *Xenopus* larvae. Rev. suisse zool., **59**:339.
FIMIAN, WALTER J. 1951. Determination of the distribution of mitotic activity in the regenerating urodele limb after partial X-irradiation. Thesis, University of Notre Dame.
GODLEWSKI, E. 1928. Untersuchungen über die Auslösung und Hemmung der Regeneration beim Axolotl. Arch. f. Entw.-Mech., **114**:108.
HELLMICH, W. 1930. Untersuchung über Herkunft und Determination des regenerative Materials bei Amphibien. Arch. Entw.-Mech., **121**:135.
HOLTZER, H., HOLTZER, S., and AVERY, G. 1955. Morphogenesis of tail vertebrae during regeneration. J. Morphol., **96**:145.
ICHIKAWA, M., and OKADA, K. 1954. Studies on the determination factors in amphibian limb regeneration. Mem. Col. Sc. Univ. Kyoto, Ser. B, **21**:23.
IDE-ROZAS, ALBERTO. 1936. Die cytologische Verhältnisse bei der Regeneration Kaulquappenextremität. Arch. Entw.-Mech., **135**:552.
INOUE, SAKAE. 1954. The mitotic rate in the regenerating epithelium of the forelimb and the dorsal skin of the adult newt. Sci. Rep., Tohoku Univ., Ser. 4, **20**:182.
KAZANCEV, W. 1934. Histologische Untersuchungen der Regenerationsprozesse an amputierten Extremitäten beim Axolotl, hauptsächlich zwecks Klärung der Frage nach der Herkunft der Zellen des Regenerats. Acad. Sc. U.R.S.S. trav. lab. zool. exper. morphol. animaux, **3**:23.
LASH, JAMES W. 1955. Studies on wound closure in urodeles. J. Exper. Zoöl., **128**:13.
LECAMP, MARCEL. 1947. Les Tissus de régénération en culture in vitro. Compt. rend. Acad. sc. Paris, **224**:674.
———. 1949. Régénération chez le Triton in vitro et in vivo. *Ibid.*, **226**:695.
LITSCHKO, E. J. 1934. Einwirkung der Röntgenstrahlen auf die Regeneration der Extremitäten des Schwanzes und eines Teiles der Dorsalflosses beim Axolotl. Akad. Nauk. U.R.S.S. trav. lab. zool. exper. morphol. animaux, **3**:101.
LITWILLER, RAYMOND. 1939. Mitotic index and size in regenerating amphibian limbs. J. Exper. Zoöl., **82**:280.

LÜSCHER, MARTIN. 1946. Die Hemmung der Regeneration durch Colchicin beim Schwanz der Xenopus-Larve und ihre entwicklungsphysiologische Wirkungsanalyse. Helvet. physiol. et pharmacol. acta, **4**:465.

LUTHER, W. 1948. Regenerationsversuche mit Hilfe von Röntgenstrahlen. Verhandl. deutsch. zool. Gesellsch., Kiel, p. 66.

MANNER, H. W. 1953. The origin of the blastema and of new tissues in regenerating forelimbs of the adult *Triturus viridescens*. J. Exper. Zoöl., **122**:229.

METTETAL, CHRISTIAN. 1939. La Régénération des membres chez la Salamandra et le Triton. Histologie et détermination. Arch. anat. hist. embryol., **28**:1.

POLEZAJEW, L. W., and GINSBURG, G. I. 1944. Investigation of ways of formation of regeneration blastema based on calculation of mitotic coefficient. Compt. rend. (Doklady) Acad. sc. U.R.S.S., **43**:315.

ROSE, F. C., QUASTLER, H., and ROSE, S. M. 1953. Regeneration of x-rayed limbs of adult *Triturus* provided with unirradiated epidermis. Anat. Rec., **117**:619.

ROSE, S. M. 1948. Epidermal dedifferentiation during blastema formation in regenerating limbs of *Triturus viridescens*. J. Exper. Zoöl., **108**:337.

SCHOTTÉ, O. E. 1939. The origin and morphogenetic potencies of regenerates. Growth Suppl. 59.

SINGER, Marcus. 1955. A study of limb regeneration in the adult newt, *Triturus*, by infusion of solutions of dye and other substances directly into the growth. J. Exper. Zoöl., **128**:185.

SKOWRON, S., and ROGUSKI, H. 1953. Tail regeneration in *Xenopus laevis* tadpoles. Bull. Acad. polon. Sc. Cl. II, **1**:15.

THORNTON, C. S. 1942. Studies on the origin of the regeneration blastema in *Triturus viridescens*. J. Exper. Zoöl., **89**:375.

TOWLE, E. W. 1901. On muscle regeneration in the limbs of *Plethodon*. Biol. Bull., **2**:289.

TRAMPUSCH, H. A. L. 1951. Regeneration inhibited by X-rays and its recovery. Proc. k. nederl. Akad. wetensch., Ser. C, **54**:373.

WALTZ, HELEN K., TULLNER, W. W., EVANS, V. J., HERTZ, ROY, and EARLE, W. R. 1954. Gonadotrophic hormone secretions from hydatid mole grown in tissue culture. J. Nat. Cancer Inst., **14**:1173.

WEISS, PAUL. 1939. Principles of development. Chicago: University of Chicago Press.

WESTFALL, B. B., EVANS, V. J., SHANNON, J. E., and EARLE, W. R. 1953. The glycogen content of cell suspensions prepared from massive tissue culture. J. Nat. Cancer Inst., **14**:655.

REFERENCES FOR PAPER IV (SINGER)

BEETSCHEN, J. C. 1952. Extension et limites du pouvoir régénérateur des membres après la métamorphose chez Xenopus laevis Daudin. Bull. biol., **86**: 88–100.

BOVET, D. 1930. Les Territoires de régénération; leurs propriétés étudiées par la méthode de déviation du nerf. Rev. suisse zool., **37**:83–145.

BUTLER, E. G. 1955. Regeneration of the urodele forelimb after reversal of its proximo-distal axis. J. Morphol., **96**:265–82.

BUTLER, E. G., and SCHOTTÉ, O. E. 1941. Histological alterations in denervated non-regenerating limbs of urodele larvae. J. Exper. Zoöl., **88**:307–41.

———. 1949. Effects of delayed denervation on regenerative activity in limbs of urodele larvae. *Ibid.*, **112**:361–91.

CHALKLEY, D. T. 1954. A quantitative histological analysis of forelimb regeneration in *Triturus viridescens*. J. Morphol., **94**:21–70.

DECK, J. D. 1955. The innervation of urodele limbs of reversed proximo-distal polarity. J. Morphol., **96**:301–32.

DENT, J. N. 1954. A study of regenerates emanating from limb transplants with reversed proximo-distal polarity in the adult newt. Anat. Rec., **118**: 841–56.

FELDBERG, W. S. 1954. VII. Transmission in the central nervous system and sensory transmission. Central and sensory transmission. Pharmacol. Rev., **6**:85–93.

GOSS, R. J. 1956. An experimental analysis of taste barbel regeneration in the catfish. J. Exper. Zoöl., **131**:27–50.

GUYÉNOT, E. 1927. Le Problème morphogénétique dans la régénération des urodèles: détermination et potentialités des régénérats. Rev. suisse zool., **34**:127–54.

GUYÉNOT, E., and SCHOTTÉ, O. 1926. Le Rôle du système nerveux dans l'édification des régénérats de pattes chez les urodèles. Compt. rend. Soc. phys. et hist. nat. Genève, **48**:32–36.

HOLMES, G. E. 1931. The influence of the nervous system on regeneration in *Nereis virens*, Sars. J. Exper. Zoöl., **60**:485–509.

KAMRIN, R. P., and SINGER, M. 1955*a*. The influence of the nerve on regeneration and maintenance of the barbel of the catfish, *Ameirus nebulosus*. J. Morphol., **96**:173–88.

———. 1955*b*. The influence of the spinal cord in regeneration of the tail of the lizard, *Anolis carolinensis*. J. Exper. Zoöl., **128**:611–27.

KIORTSIS, V. 1953. Potentialités du territoire patte chez le Triton. Rev. suisse zool., **60**:301–409.

KORSCHELT, E. 1927. Regeneration and transplantation, **1**:593–620. Berlin: Borntraeger.

LENDER, TH. 1955. Mise en évidence et propriétés de l'organisme de la régénération des yeux chez la planaire Polycelis nigra. Rev. suisse zool., **62**: 268–75.

LOCATELLI, P. 1924. L'Influenza del sistema nervoso sui processi di regenerazione. Arch. sc. biol., **5**:362–78.

———. 1929. Der Einfluss des Nervensystems auf die Regeneration. Arch. Entw.-Mech., **114**:686–770.

LOEWI, O., and HELLAUER, H. 1938. Über das Acetylcholin in peripheren Nerven. Arch. f. d. ges. Physiol., **240**:769–75.

LUTHER, W. 1948. Regenerationsversuche mit Hilfe von Röntgenstrahlen. Verhandl. deutsch. zool. Gesellsch., Kiel, pp. 67–68.

MORGAN, T. H. 1902. Experimental studies of the internal factors of regeneration of the earthworm. Arch. f. Entw.-Mech., **14**:563–91.

———. 1906–7. The extent and limitations of the power to regenerate in man and other vertebrates. Harvey Lect. (1905–6), pp. 219–29.

———. 1908. Experiments in grafting. Am. Naturalist, **42**:1–11.

NEEDHAM, A. E. 1952. Regeneration and wound-healing. (Methuen Monograph.) London: Methuen.

ORECHOWITSCH, W. N., and BROMLEY, N. W. 1934. Die histolysierenden Eigenschaften des Regenerationsblastems. Biol. Zentralbl., **54**:524–35.

PARKER, G. H. 1932. On the trophic impulse, so-called, its rate and nature. Am. Naturalist, **66**:147–58.

Polezaiev, L. W. 1946. The loss and restoration of regenerative capacity in the limbs of tailless Amphibia. Biol. Rev. (Cambridge Phil. Soc.), **21**: 141–47.

Rose, F. C., Quastler, H., and Rose, S. M. 1955. Regeneration of X-rayed salamander limbs provided with normal epidermis. Science, **122**:1018–19.

Rose, S. M. 1945. The effect of NaCl in stimulating regeneration of limbs of frogs. J. Morphol., **77**:119–39.

———. 1948*a*. The role of nerves in amphibian limb regeneration. Ann. New York Acad. Sc., **49**:818–33.

———. 1948*b*. Epidermal dedifferentiation during blastema formation in regenerating limbs of *Triturus viridescens*. J. Exper. Zoöl., **108**:337–61.

Rostand, J. 1932. De la faculté régénératrice chez *Xenopus laevis*. Compt. rend. Soc. biol., **111**:451.

Schotté, O. E. 1926. Nouvelles preuves physiologiques de l'action du système nerveux sympathique dans la régénération. Compt. rend. Soc. hist. nat., Genève, **43**:140.

Schotté, O. E., and Butler, E. G. 1941. Morphological effects of denervation and amputation of limbs in urodele larvae. J. Exper. Zoöl., **87**:279–322.

———. 1944. Phases in regeneration of the urodele limb and their dependence upon the nervous system. *Ibid.*, **97**:95–121.

Schotté, O. E., Butler, E. G., and Hood, R. T. 1941. Effects of transplanted blastemas on amputated nerveless limbs of urodele larvae. Proc. Soc. Exper. Biol. & Med., **48**:500–503.

Schotté, O. E., and Harland, M. 1943. Effects of denervation and amputation of hind limbs in anuran tadpoles. J. Exper. Zoöl., **93**:453–93.

Singer, M. 1943. The nervous system and regeneration of the forelimb of adult *Triturus*. II. The role of the sensory supply. J. Exper. Zoöl., **92**: 297–315.

———. 1946. The nervous system and regeneration of the forelimb of adult *Triturus*. V. The influence of number of nerve fibers, including a quantitative study of limb innervation. *Ibid.*, **101**:299–337.

———. 1949*a*. The invasion of the epidermis of the regenerating forelimb of the urodele, *Triturus*, by nerve fibers. Anat. Rec., **103**:506.

———. 1949*b*. The invasion of the epidermis of the regenerating forelimb of the urodele, *Triturus*, by nerve fibers. J. Exper. Zoöl., **111**:189–210.

———. 1952. The influence of the nerve in regeneration of the amphibian extremity. Quart. Rev. Biol., **27**:169–200.

———. 1954*a*. Apparatus for continuous infusion of microvolumes of solution into organs and tissues. Proc. Soc. Exper. Biol. & Med., **86**:378–80.

———. 1954*b*. Induction of regeneration of the forelimb of the postmetamorphic frog by augmentation of the nerve supply. J. Exper. Zoöl., **126**:419–71.

Singer, M., and Craven, L. 1948. The growth and morphogenesis of the regenerating forelimb of adult *Triturus* following denervation at various stages of development. J. Exper. Zoöl., **108**:279–308.

Singer, M., and Kamrin, R. P. 1954. The influence of denervation on induction of limb regeneration by hypertonic salt solutions in the postmetamorphic frog, including some observations on denervated salt-treated salamander limbs. Anat. Rec., **120**:700–701.

Singer, M., Scheuing, M., and Hall, M. 1953. A microinfusion apparatus for regeneration studies and its use in the study of the nature of the influence which nerves exert on regeneration of the limb of the adult newt. Anat. Rec., **117**:576.

SINGER, M., WEINBERG, A., and SIDMAN, R. L. 1955. A study of limb regeneration in the adult newt, *Triturus*, by infusion of solutions of dye and other substances directly into the growth. J. Exper. Zoöl., **128**:185–217.

SPALLANZANI, A. 1769. An essay on animal reproductions. (Translated from the Italian, 1768, by M. MATY.) London.

TABAN, C. 1949. Les Fibres nerveuses et l'épithélium dans l'édification des régénérats de pattes (in situ ou induites) chez le Triton. Arch. sc., **2**:553–61.

———. 1955. Quelques problémes de régénération chez les urodèles. Rev. suisse zool., **62**:387–468.

TAUBE, E. 1923. Über die histologischen Vorgänge bei der Regeneration von Tritonen mit Beteiligung ortsfremder Haut. Arch. mikr. Anat., **98**:98–120.

THORNTON, C. S. 1938. The histogenesis of muscle in the regenerating forelimb of larval *Amblystoma punctatum*. J. Morphol., **62**:17–47.

———. 1942. Studies on the origin of the regeneration blastema in *Triturus viridescens*. J. Exper. Zoöl., **89**:375–89.

———. 1953. Histological modifications in denervated injured forelimbs of *Amblystoma* larvae. *Ibid.*, **122**:119–50.

———. 1954. The relation of epidermal innervation to limb regeneration in *Amblystoma* larvae. *Ibid.*, **127**:577–602.

———. 1956. Epidermal modifications in regenerating and in non-regenerating limbs of anuran larvae. *Ibid.*, **131**:373–94.

THORNTON, C. S., and KRAEMER, D. W. 1951. The effect of injury on denervated unamputated forelimbs of *Amblystoma* larvae. J. Exper. Zoöl., **117**:415–40.

TODD, TWEEDY JOHN. 1823. On the process of reproduction of the members of the aquatic salamander. Quart. J. Sc. Arts & Lit. **16**:84–96.

TRAMPUSCH, H. A. L. 1951. Regeneration inhibited by X-rays and its recovery. Proc. k. nederl. Akad. wetensch., Ser. C, **54**:3–15.

VAN STONE, J. M. 1955. The relationship between innervation and regenerative capacity in hind limbs of *Rana sylvatica*. J. Morphol., **97**:345–92.

WELSH, J. H. 1946. Evidence of a trophic action of acetylcholine in a planarian. Anat. Rec., **94**:421.

WOLFGRAM, F. J. 1954. Relative amounts of choline acetylase and choline sterases in dorsal and ventral roots of cattle. Am. J. Physiol., **176**:505–7.

WOODLAND, W. N. F. 1920. Some observations on caudal autonomy and regeneration in the gecko (*Hemidactylus flaviviridis*, Ruppel), with notes on the tails of *Sphenodon* and *Pygapus*. Quart. J. Micr. Sc., **65**:63–100.

YNTEMA, C. L. 1949. Relations between innervation and regeneration of the forelimb in urodele larvae. Anat. Rec., **103**:524.

REFERENCES FOR PAPER VI (TRAMPUSCH)

BUTLER, E. G. 1933. The effects of X-radiation on the regeneration of the forelimb of *Amblystoma* larvae. J. Exper. Zoöl., **65**:271.

BUTLER, E. G., and O'BRIEN, J. P. 1942. Effects of localized X-radiation on regeneration of the urodele limb. Anat. Rec. **84**:407.

BUTLER, E. G., and PUCKETT, W. O. 1940. Studies on cellular interaction during limb regeneration in *Amblystoma*. J. Exper. Zoöl., **84**:223.

CHIAKULAS, J. J. 1952, The role of tissue specificity in the healing of epithelial wounds. J. Exper. Zoöl., **121**:383.

HELLMICH, W. 1929. Untersuchungen über die Herkunft und Determination des regenerativen Materiales bei Amphibien. Roux Arch. f. Entw., **121**:135.

HERTWIG, G. 1927. Beiträge zum Determinations- und Regenerations problem mittels der Transplantation haploidkerniger Zellen. Roux Arch. f. Entw., **111**:292.

LASH, J. W. 1955. Studies on wound closure in urodeles. J. Exper. Zoöl., **128**:13.

NEEDHAM, A. E. 1941. Some experimental biological uses of the element beryllium. Proc. Zool. Soc. London, A, **111**:59.

POLEZAJEW, L. W. 1939. On the mode of restoration of regenerative power in the limbs of tailless amphibians. Compt. rend. Acad. sc. U.S.S.R., **22**:648.

THORNTON, C. S. 1949. Beryllium inhibition of regeneration. I. Morphological effects of beryllium on amputated forelimbs of larval *Amblystoma*. J. Morphol., **84**:459.

———. 1951. III. Histological effects of beryllium on the amputated forelimb of *Amblystoma* larvae. J. Exper. Zoöl., **118**:467.

TRAMPUSCH, H. A. L. 1951. Regeneration inhibited by X-rays and its recovery. Proc. k. nederl. Akad. wetensch., Ser. C, **54**:373.

TUCHMANN-DUPLESSIS, H. 1950. Action de sels de beryllium sur le régénération chez le Triton. Bull. hist. appl. et techn. micr., **27**:116.

WEISS, P. 1950. Perspectives in the field of morphogenesis. Quart. Rev. Biol., **25**:1777.

PRINTED IN U.S.A.